SLAVE SONGS

OF THE

UNITED STATES

New York:
A. SIMPSON & CO.,
1867.

PUBLISHER'S FOREWORD

SLAVE SONGS OF THE UNITED STATES is one of the great documents of America. Published shortly after the end of the Civil War, the songs were collected during the war, mostly from among Negroes living on the Islands off the coast of Georgia and South Carolina.

This new edition of SLAVE SONGS OF THE UNITED STATES is published at a most appropriate moment in our history. The tremendous tasks undertaken by the Emancipation Proclamation and Reconstruction are closer to fulfillment than at any other time. There is renewed interest in the life and culture of the Negro slaves. In particular, there is interest in the music of that period -- since so much contemporary musical expression of jazz, swing, rhythm-and-blues, rock-and-roll, and modern gospel song has its roots in these songs.

Because of this, we have not attempted to "translate" the original songs from the transcribed dialect into a more commonly-accepted usage. Rather, we believe that those who will sing these songs will make their own adaptations of the words. Similarly, the introduction has been photographically reproduced from the original edition. This section has remained intact, even to the archaic spelling of the word "Negro" with a small "n."

Today, when the songs of the Freedom Movement are heard in the churches and on the highways of the South, these songs serve as an inspiration and a memory of the living heart of history.

SLAVE SONGS OF THE UNITED STATES

The complete original collection (136 songs) collected and compiled by
William Francis Allen, Charles Pickard Ware and Lucy McKim Garrison in 1867,
with new piano accompaniments and guitar chords by IRVING SCHLEIN

OAK PUBLICATIONS

Guitar chords and music editing Jerry Silverman
Paste-Up and Production Jean Hammond
Illustrations selected by Irwin Silber

© 1965 Oak Publications
165 West 46th St., New York, N.Y.

Library of Congress Catalogue Card Number: 6522693

Printed in the United States of America for the Publisher
by Faculty Press, Inc., Brooklyn, N.Y.

FOREWORD

The Slave Songs are in large measure a reflection of the suffering and deprivation the Negro slaves had to endure before their emancipation. "... the wild, sad strains tell, as the sufferers themselves could, of crushed hopes, keen sorrow, and a dull, daily misery which covered them as hopelessly as the fog from the rice swamps." They achieved in song what was denied them in real life: salvation and release from the daily, inhuman torture they had to endure at the hands of their white masters.

Strange indeed, that these identical Slave Songs should become the bedrock out of which our American music grew. The fructifying influence of the "sperichels" had its effect on no less a composer than Anton Dvorak, a Bohemian by birth, who came to this country in the late 90's, wrote the "New World" Symphony, in which he used Negro folk songs; this in turn became the beacon-light for the native American composer whom he awakened to the realization that in the Negro folk songs was embedded a rich source of inspiration.

The Slave Songs were first collected in book form by Allen, Ware and Garrison, in 1867. They appeared in their natural, melodic state without accompaniment, or any indication of chords. Since then they have remained in their pristine state, most of them as oddities encased in the archives of folklore societies. The venture was, according to the editors, the first attempt "to collect and preserve their (the Negro people's) melodies." For the most part, the melodies were "taken down...from the lips of the colored people themselves...some may even appear as variants of older melodies acquired in darkest Africa, and brought here by the slaves. As for the words, only one set was arranged by the editors to each melody; for the rest, one must make them fit the best he can, as the negroes themselves do."

My aim, at present, is to bring the Slave Songs out into the light, to release them from their one-hundred-year imprisonment by adding piano accompaniments to them. Singers can now sing the songs, with the comforting support of a piano background.

The question arises as to what would be the most appropriate type of accompaniment. There are generally two kinds: the arranger's and the composer's. The former writes a simple, unobtrusive harmonic background that permits the melody to soar freely, while the latter creates an original accompaniment that is more a reflection of the composer's mood and feeling engendered by the melody. The harmony becomes more colorful, with the added danger however that the simplicity and charm of the original melody may be lost amidst a welter of 'modernisms'. In these harmonizations I have tried to steer a middle course: I have allowed my imagination to expand within the bounds of reason and restraint. I have never lost sight of the simplicity of melody and words, which are of utmost importance in the Slave Songs. Nonetheless, modernisms may creep in as they do, very subtly. Perhaps, in future editions, other writers will refashion the songs in quite different harmonies, but the innate beauty of the Slave Songs themselves will always emerge through any kind of accompaniment. They are a tribute to a people who, one hundred years after their emancipation from slavery, are still fighting to secure the rights and privileges due every American citizen, regardless of the color of his skin.

IRVING SCHLEIN

CONTENTS

The material on the following pages is photographically reproduced from the original edition of

SLAVE SONGS OF THE UNITED STATES

The musical capacity of the negro race has been recognized for so many years that it is hard to explain why no systematic effort has hitherto been made to collect and preserve their melodies. More than thirty years ago those plantation songs made their appearance which were so extraordinarily popular for a while; and if "Coal-black Rose," "Zip Coon" and "Ole Virginny nebber tire" have been succeeded by spurious imitations, manufactured to suit the somewhat sentimental taste of our community, the fact that these were called "negro melodies" was itself a tribute to the musical genius of the race. *

The public had well-nigh forgotten these genuine slave songs, and with them the creative power from which they sprung, when a fresh interest was excited through the educational mission to the Port Royal islands, in 1861. The agents of this mission were not long in dis-

---

*It is not generally known that the beautiful air "Long time ago," or "Near the lake where drooped the willow," was borrowed from the negroes, by whom it was sung to words beginning, "Way down in Raccoon Hollow."

ii covering the rich vein of music that existed in these half-barbarous people, and when visitors from the North were on the islands, there was nothing that seemed better worth their while than to see a "shout" or hear the "people" sing their "sperichils." A few of these last, of special merit,* soon became established favorites among the whites, and hardly a Sunday passed at the church on St. Helena without "Gabriel's Trumpet," "I hear from Heaven to-day," or "Jehovah Hallelujah." The last time I myself heard these was at the Fourth of July celebration, at the church, in 1864. All of them were sung, and then the glorious shout, "I can't stay behind, my Lord," was struck up, and sung by the entire multitude with a zest and spirit, a swaying of the bodies and nodding of the heads and lighting of the countenances and rhythmical movement of the hands, which I think no one present will ever forget.

Attention was, I believe, first publicly directed to these songs in a letter from Miss McKim, of Philadelphia, to *Dwight's Journal of Music*, Nov. 8, 1862, from which some extracts will presently be given. At about the same time, Miss McKim arranged and published two of them, "Roll, Jordan" (No. 1) and "Poor Rosy" (No. 8) —probably on all accounts the two best specimens that could be selected. Mr. H. G. Spaulding not long after gave some well-chosen specimens of the music in an article entitled "Under the Palmetto," in the *Continental*

---

*The first seven spirituals in this collection, which were regularly sung at the church.

Monthly for August, 1863, among them, "O Lord, re- iii member me" (No. 15), and "The Lonesome Valley" (No. 7). Many other persons interested themselves in the collection of words and tunes, and it seems time at last that the partial collections in the possession of the editors, and known by them to be in the possession of others, should not be forgotten and lost, but that these relics of a state of society which has passed away should be preserved while it is still possible.*

The greater part of the music here presented has been taken down by the editors from the lips of the colored people themselves; when we have obtained it from other sources, we have given credit in the table of contents. The largest and most accurate single collection in existence is probably that made by Mr. Charles P. Ware, chiefly at Coffin's Point, St. Helena Island. We have thought it best to give this collection in its entirety, as the basis of the present work; it includes all the hymns as far as No. 43. Those which follow, as far as No. 55, were collected by myself on the Capt. John Fripp and neighboring plantations, on the same island. In all cases we have added words from other sources and other localities, when they could be obtained, as well as variations of the tunes wherever they were of sufficient importance to warrant it. Of the other hymns and songs

---

*Only this last spring a valuable collection of songs made at Richmond, Va., was lost in the *Wagner*. No copy had been made from the original manuscript so that the labor of their collection was lost. We had hoped to have the use of them in preparing the present work.

we have given the locality whenever it could be ascer- iv tained.

The difficulty experienced in attaining absolute correctness is greater than might be supposed by those who have never tried the experiment, and we are far from claiming that we have made no mistakes. I have never felt quite sure of my notation without a fresh comparison with the singing, and have then often found that I had made some errors. I feel confident, however, that there are no mistakes of importance. What may appear to some to be an incorrect rendering, is very likely to be a variation; for these variations are endless, and very entertaining and instructive.

Neither should any one be repelled by any difficulty in adapting the words to the tunes. The negroes keep exquisite time in singing, and do not suffer themselves to be daunted by any obstacle in the words. The most obstinate Scripture phrases or snatches from hymns they will force to do duty with any tune they please, and will dash heroically through a trochaic tune at the head of a column of iambs with wonderful skill. We have in all cases arranged one set of words carefully to each melody; for the rest, one must make them fit the best he can, as the negroes themselves do.

The best that we can do, however, with paper and types, or even with voices, will convey but a faint shadow of the original. The voices of the colored people have a peculiar quality that nothing can imitate; and the intonations and delicate variations of even one singer cannot be reproduced on paper. And I despair of conveying any notion of the effect of a number singing together, especially in a complicated shout, like "I can't stay behind, my Lord" (No. 8), or "Turn, sinner, turn O!" (No. 48). There is no singing in *parts*,* as we understand it, and yet no two appear to be singing the same thing—the leading singer starts the words of each verse, often improvising, and the others, who "base" him, as it is called, strike in with the refrain, or even join in the solo, when the words are familiar. When the "base" begins, the leader often stops, leaving the rest of his words to be guessed at, or it may be they are taken up by one of the other singers. And the "basers" themselves seem to follow their own whims, beginning when they please and leaving off when they please, striking an octave above or below (in case they have pitched the tune too low or too high), or hitting some other note that chords, so as to produce the effect of a marvellous complication and variety, and yet with the most perfect time, and rarely with any discord. And what makes it all the harder to unravel a thread of melody out of this strange network is that, like birds, they seem not infrequently to strike sounds that cannot be precisely represented by the gamut, and abound in

---

* "The high voices, all in unison, and the admirable time and true accent with which their responses are made, always make me wish that some great musical composer could hear these semi-savage performances. With a very little skilful adaptation and instrumentation, I think one or two barbaric chants and choruses might be evoked from them that would make the fortune of an opera."—*Mrs. Kemble's "Life on a Georgian Plantation," p. 218.*

"slides from one note to another, and turns and cadences not in articulated notes." "It is difficult," writes Miss McKim, "to express the entire character of these negro ballads by mere musical notes and signs. The odd turns made in the throat, and the curious rhythmic effect produced by single voices chiming in at different irregular intervals, seem almost as impossible to place on the score as the singing of birds or the tones of an Æolian Harp." There are also apparent irregularities in the time, which it is no less difficult to express accurately, and of which Nos. 10, 130, 131, and (eminently) 128, are examples.

Still, the chief part of the negro music is *civilized* in its character—partly composed under the influence of association with the whites, partly actually imitated from their music. In the main it appears to be original in the best sense of the word, and the more we examine the subject, the more genuine it appears to us to be. In a very few songs, as Nos. 19, 23, and 25, strains of familiar tunes are readily traced; and it may easily be that others contain strains of less familiar music, which the slaves heard their masters sing or play.*

On the other hand there are very few which are of an intrinsically barbaric character, and where this character does appear, it is chiefly in short passages, intermingled

---

* We have rejected as spurious "Give me Jesus," "Climb Jacob's Ladder," (both sung at Port Royal), and "I'll take the wings of the morning," which we find in Methodist hymn-books. A few others, the character of which seemed somewhat suspicious, we have not felt at liberty to reject without direct evidence

with others of a different character. Such passages may be found perhaps in Nos. 10, 12, and 18; and "Becky Lawton," for instance (No. 29), "Shall I die?" (No. 52) "Round the corn, Sally" (No. 87), and "O'er the crossing" (No. 93) may very well be purely African in origin. Indeed, it is very likely that if we had found it possible to get at more of their secular music, we should have come to another conclusion as to the proportion of the barbaric element. A gentleman in Delaware writes:

"We must look among their non-religious songs for the purest specimens of negro minstrelsy. It is remarkable that they have themselves transferred the best of these to the uses of their churches—I suppose on Mr. Wesley's principle that 'it is not right the Devil should have all the good tunes.' Their leaders and preachers have not found this change difficult to effect; or at least they have taken so little pains about it that one often detects the profane *cropping out*, and revealing the origin of their most solemn 'hymns,' in spite of the best intentions of the poet and artist. Some of the best *pure negro* songs I have ever heard were those that used to be sung by the black stevedores, or perhaps the crews themselves, of the West India vessels, loading and unloading at the wharves in Philadelphia and Baltimore. I have stood for more than an hour, often, listening to them, as they hoisted and lowered the hogsheads and boxes of their cargoes; one man taking the burden of the song (and the slack of the rope) and the others striking in with the chorus. They would sing in this

way more than a dozen different songs in an hour; most of which might indeed be warranted to contain 'nothing religious'—a few of them, 'on the contrary, quite the reverse'—but generally rather innocent and proper in their language, and strangely attractive in their music; and with a volume of voice that reached a square or two away. That plan of labor has now passed away, in Philadelphia at least, and the songs, I suppose, with it. So that these performances are to be heard only among black sailors on their vessels, or 'long-shore men in out-of-the-way places, where opportunities for respectable persons to hear them are rather few."

These are the songs that are still heard upon the Mississippi steamboats—wild and strangely fascinating—one of which we have been so fortunate as to secure for this collection. This, too, is no doubt the music of the colored firemen of Savannah, graphically described by Mr. Kane O'Donnel, in a letter to the Philadelphia *Press*, and one of which he was able to contribute for our use. Mr. E. S. Philbrick was struck with the resemblance of some of the rowing tunes at Port-Royal to the boatmen's songs he had heard upon the Nile.

The greater number of the songs which have come into our possession seem to be the natural and original production of a race of remarkable musical capacity and very teachable, which has been long enough associated with the more cultivated race to have become imbued with the mode and spirit of European music—often, nevertheless, retaining a distinct tinge of their native Africa.

The words are, of course, in a large measure taken from Scripture, and from the hymns heard at church; and for this reason these religious songs do not by any means illustrate the full extent of the debasement of the .dialect. Such expressions as "Cross Jordan," "O Lord, remember me," "I'm going home," "There's room enough in Heaven for you," we find abundantly in Methodist hymn-books; but with much searching I have been able to find hardly a trace of the tunes. The words of the fine hymn, "Praise, member" (No. 5), are found, with very little variation, in "Choral Hymns" (No. 138). The editor of this collection informs us, however, that many of his songs were learned from negroes in Philadelphia, and Lt.-Col. Trowbridge tells us that he heard this hymn, before the war, among the colored people of Brooklyn.* For some very comical specimens of the way in which half-understood words and phrases are distorted by them, see Nos. 22, 23. Another illustration is given by Col. Higginson :†

"The popular camp-song of 'Marching Along' was entirely new to them until our quartermaster taught it to them at my request. The words 'Gird on the armor' were to them a stumbling-block, and no wonder, until

---

* We have generally preserved the words as sung, even where clearly nonsensical, as in No. 89; so "Why don't you move so slow?" (No. 22). We will add that "Paul and Silas, bound in jail" (No. 4), is often sung "Bounden Cyrus born in jail," and the words of No. 11 would appear as "I take my tex in Matchew and by de Revolutions—I know you by your gammon," &c.; so "Ringy Rosy Land" for "Ring Jerusalem."
† *Atlantic Monthly*, June, 1867.

---

some ingenious ear substituted 'Guide on de army,' which was at once accepted and became universal. 'We'll guide on de army, and be marching along,' is now the established version on the Sea Islands."

I never fairly heard a secular song among the Port Royal freedmen, and never saw a musical instrument among them. The last violin, owned by a "worldly man," disappeared from Coffin's Point "de year gun shoot at Bay Pint."* In other parts of the South, "fiddle-sings," "devil-songs," "corn-songs," "jig-tunes," and what not, are common; all the world knows the banjo, and the "Jim Crow" songs of thirty years ago. We have succeeded in obtaining only a very few songs of this character. Our intercourse with the colored people has been chiefly through the work of the Freedmen's Commission, which deals with the serious and earnest side of the negro character. It is often, indeed, no easy matter to persuade them to sing their old songs, even as a curiosity, such is the sense of dignity that has come with freedom. It is earnestly to be desired that some person, who has the opportunity, should make a collection of these now, before it is too late.

In making the present collection, we have only gleaned upon the surface, and in a very narrow field. The wealth of material still awaiting the collector can be guessed from a glance at the localities of those we have, and from

---

* *i. e.*, November, 1861, when Hilton Head was taken by Admiral Dupont—a great date on the islands.

---

the fact, mentioned above, that of the first forty-three of the collection most were sung upon a single plantation, and that it is very certain that the stores of this plantation were by no means exhausted. Of course there was constant intercourse between neighboring plantations; also between different States, by the sale of slaves from one to another. But it is surprising how little this seems to have affected local songs, which are different even upon adjoining plantations. The favorite of them all, "Roll, Jordan" (No. 1), is sung in Florida, but not, I believe, in North Carolina. "Gabriel's Trumpet" (No. 4) and "Wrestle on, Jacob" (No 6) probably came from Virginia, where they are sung without much variation from the form usual at Port Royal; No. 6 is also sung in Maryland.* "John, John of the Holy Order" (No. 22) is traced in Georgia and North Carolina, and "O'er the Crossing" (No. 93) appears to be the Virginia original, variations of which are found in South Carolina, Georgia, and Tennessee. As illustrations of the slowness with which these songs travel, it may be mentioned that the "Graveyard" (No. 21), which was frequently sung on Capt. John Fripp's plantation in the winter of 1863-4, did not reach Coffin's Point (five miles distant) until the following Spring. I heard it myself at Pine Grove, two miles from the latter place, in March. Somewhere

---

* It is worthy of notice that a song much resembling "Poor Rosy" was heard last Spring from the boat hands of an Ohio River steamboat—the only words caught being "Poor Molly, poor gal."

---

upon this journey this tune was strikingly altered, as will be seen from the variation given, which is the form in which I was accustomed to hear it. Nos. 38, 41, 42, 43, 118, 119, 122, 123, were brought to Coffin's Point after Mr. Ware left, by refugees returning to the plantation from "town" and the Main. No. 74, likewise, "Nobody knows the trouble I see," which was common in Charleston in 1865, has since been carried to Coffin's Point, very little altered.

These hymns will be found peculiarly interesting in illustrating the feelings, opinions and habits of the slaves. Of the dialect I shall presently speak at some length. One of their customs, often alluded to in the songs (as in No. 19), is that of wandering through the woods and swamps, when under religious excitement, like the ancient bacchantes. To get religion is with them to "fin' dat ting." Molsy described thus her sister's experience in searching for religion: "Couldn't fin' dat leetle ting—hunt for 'em—huntin' for 'em all de time—las' foun' 'em." And one day, on our way to see a "shout," we asked Bristol whether he was going :—"No, ma'am, wouldn't let me in—hain't foun' dat ting yet—hain't been on my knees in de swamp." Of technical religious expressions, "seeker," "believer," "member," &c., the songs are full.

The most peculiar and interesting of their customs is the "shout," an excellent description of which we are permitted to copy from the N. Y. *Nation* of May 30, 1867:

"This is a ceremony which the white clergymen are inclined to discountenance, and even of the colored elders some of the more discreet try sometimes to put on a face of discouragement; and although, if pressed for Biblical warrant for the shout, they generally seem to think 'he in de Book,' or 'he dere-da in Matchew,' still it is not considered blasphemous or improper if 'de chillen' and 'dem young gal' carry it on in the evening for amusement's sake, and with no well-defined intention of 'praise.' But the true 'shout' takes place on Sundays or on 'praise'-nights through the week, and either in the praise-house'or in some cabin in which a regular religious meeting has been held. Very likely more than half the population of the plantation is gathered together. Let it be the evening, and a light-wood fire burns red before the door of the house and on the hearth. For some time one can hear, though at a good distance, the vociferous exhortation or prayer of the presiding elder or of the brother who has a gift that way, and who is not 'on the back seat,'—a phrase, the interpretation of which is, 'under the censure of the church authorities for bad behavior;'—and at regular intervals one hears the elder 'deaconing' a hymn-book hymn, which is sung two lines at a time, and whose wailing cadences, borne on the night air, are indescribably melancholy. But the benches are pushed back to the wall when the formal meeting is over, and old and young, men and women, sprucely-dressed young men, grotesquely half-clad field-hands—the women generally with gay handkerchiefs twisted about their heads and with short skirts—boys with tattered shirts and men's trousers, young girls bare-

footed, all stand up in the middle of the floor, and when the 'sperichil' is struck up, begin first walking and by-and-by shuffling round, one after the other, in a ring. The foot is hardly taken from the floor, and the progression is mainly due to a jerking, hitching motion, which agitates the entire shouter, and soon brings out streams of perspiration. Sometimes they dance silently, sometimes as they shuffle they sing the chorus of the spiritual, and sometimes the song itself is also sung by the dancers. But more frequently a band, composed of some of the best singers and of tired shouters, stand at the side of the room to 'base' the others, singing the body of the song and clapping their hands together or on the knees. Song and dance are alike extremely energetic, and often, when the shout lasts into the middle of the night, the monotonous thud, thud of the feet prevents sleep within half a mile of the praise-house."

In the form here described, the "shout" is probably confined to South Carolina and the States south of it. It appears to be found in Florida, but not in North Carolina or Virginia. It is, however, an interesting fact that the term "shouting" is used in Virginia in reference to a peculiar motion of the body not wholly unlike the Carolina shouting. It is not unlikely that this remarkable religious ceremony is a relic of some native African dance, as the Romaika is of the classical Pyrrhic. Dancing in the usual way is regarded with great horror by the people of Port Royal, but they enter with infinite zest into the movements of the "shout." It has its

connoisseurs, too. "Jimmy great shouter," I was told; and Jimmy himself remarked to me, as he looked patronizingly on a ring of young people, "Dese yere worry deyseff—we don't worry weseff." And indeed, although the perspiration streamed copiously down his shiny face, he shuffled round the circle with great ease and grace.

The shouting may be to any tune, and perhaps all the Port Royal hymns here given are occasionally used for this purpose; so that our cook's classification into "sperichils" and "runnin' sperichils" (shouts), or the designation of certain ones as sung "just sittin' round, you know," will hardly hold in strictness. In practice, however, a distinction is generally observed. The first seven, for instance, favorite hymns in the St. Helena church, would rarely, if ever, be used for shouting; while probably on each plantation there is a special set in common use. On my plantation I oftenest heard "Pray all de member" (No. 47), "Bell da ring" (No. 46), "Shall I die?" (No. 52), and "I can't stay behind, my Lord" (No. 8). The shouting step varied with the tune; one could hardly dance with the same spirit to "Turn, sinner," or "My body rock 'long fever," as to "Rock o' Jubilee," or "O Jerusalem, early in de morning." So far as I can learn, the shouting is confined to the Baptists; and it is, no doubt, to the overwhelming preponderance of this denomination on the Sea Islands that we owe the peculiar richness and originality of the music there

The same songs are used for rowing as for shouting. I know only one pure boat-song, the fine lyric, "Michael row the boat ashore" (No. 31); and this I have no doubt is a real spiritual—it being the archangel Michael that is addressed. Among the most common rowing tunes were Nos. 5, 14, 17, 27, 28, 29, 30, 31, 32, 33, 36, 46. "As I have written these tunes," says Mr. Ware, "two measures are to be sung to each stroke, the first measure being accented by the beginning of the stroke, the second by the rattle of the oars in the rowlocks. On the passenger boat at the [Beaufort] ferry, they rowed from sixteen to thirty strokes a minute; twenty-four was the average. Of the tunes I have heard, I should say that the most lively were 'Heaven bell a-ring' (No. 27), 'Jine 'em' (No. 28), 'Rain fall' (No. 29), 'No man' (No. 14), 'Bell da ring' (No. 46), and 'Can't stay behind;' and that 'Lay this body down' (No. 26), 'Religion so sweet' (No. 17), and 'Michael row' (No. 31), were used when the load was heavy or the tide was against us. I think that the long hold on 'Oh,' in 'Rain fall,' was only used in rowing. When used as a 'shout' I am quite sure that it occupied only one measure, as in the last part of the verse. One noticeable thing about their boat-songs was that they seemed often to be sung just a trifle behind time; in 'Rain fall,' for instance, 'Believer cry holy' would seem to occupy more than its share of the stroke, the 'holy' being prolonged till the very beginning of the next stroke; indeed, I think Jerry often hung on his oar a little just there before dipping it again."*

As to the composition of these songs, "I always wondered," says Col. Higginson, "whether they had always a conscious and definite origin in some leading mind, or whether they grew by gradual accretion, in an almost unconscious way. On this point I could get no information, though I asked many questions, until at last, one day when I was being rowed across from Beaufort to Ladies' Island, I found myself, with delight, on the actual trail of a song. One of the oarsmen, a brisk young fellow, not a soldier, on being asked for his theory of the matter, dropped out a coy confession. 'Some good speritials,' he said, 'are start jess out o' curiosity. I been a-raise a sing, myself, once.'

"My dream was fulfilled, and I had traced out, not the poem alone, but the poet. I implored him to proceed.

"'Once we boys,' he said, 'went for tote some rice, and de nigger-driver, he keep a-callin' on us; and I say, 'O, de ole nigger-driver!' Den anudder said, 'Fust ting my mammy told me was, notin' so bad as nigger-drivers.' Den I made a sing, just puttin' a word, and den anudder word.'

"Then he began singing, and the men, after listening a moment, joined in the chorus as if it were an old ac-

---

* For another curious circumstance in rowing, see note to "Rain fall," No. 29.

quaintance, though they evidently had never heard it before. I saw how easily a new 'sing' took root among them."

A not inconsistent explanation is that given on page 12 of an "Address delivered by J. Miller McKim, in Sansom Hall, Philadelphia, July 9, 1862."

"I asked one of these blacks—one of the most intelligent of them [Prince Rivers, Sergeant 1st Reg. S. C. V.]—where they got these songs. 'Dey make 'em, sah.' 'How do they make them?' After a pause, evidently casting about for an explanation, he said: 'I'll tell you, it's dis way. My master call me up, and order me a short peck of corn and a hundred lash. My friends see it, and is sorry for me. When dey come to de praise-meeting dat night dey sing about it. Some's very good singers and know how; and dey work it in—work it in, you know, till they get it right; and dat's de way.' A very satisfactory explanation; at least so it seemed to me."

We were not so fortunate as Col. Higginson in our search for a poet. Cuffee at Pine Grove did, to be sure, confess himself the author of "Climb Jacob's Ladder;"—unfortunately, we afterwards found it in a Northern hymn book. And if you try to trace out a new song, and ask, "Where did you hear that?" the answer will be, "One strange man come from Eding's las' praise-night and sing 'em in praise-house, and de people catch 'em;" or "Titty 'Mitta [sister Amaritta] fetch 'em from Polawana, where she tuk her walk gone spend Sunday. Some of her fahmly sing 'em yonder." "But what does

'Ringy rosy land' [Ring Jerusalem, No. 21] mean?" "Me dunno."

Our title, "Slave Songs," was selected because it best described the contents of the book. A few of those here given (Nos. 64, 59) were, to be sure, composed since the proclamation of emancipation, but even these were inspired by slavery. "All, indeed, are valuable as an expression of the character and life of the race which is playing such a conspicuous part in our history. The wild, sad strains tell, as the sufferers themselves could, of crushed hopes, keen sorrow, and a dull, daily misery, which covered them as hopelessly as the fog from the rice swamps. On the other hand, the words breathe a trusting faith in rest for the future—in 'Canaan's air and happy land,' to which their eyes seem constantly turned."

Our original plan hardly contemplated more than the publication of the Port Royal spirituals, some sixty in all, which we had supposed we could obtain, with perhaps a few others in an appendix. As new materials came into our hands, we enlarged our plan to the present dimensions. Next to South Carolina, we have the largest number from Virginia; from the other States comparatively few. Few as they are, however, they appear to indicate a very distinct character in different States. Contrary to what might be expected, the songs from Virginia are the most wild and strange. "O'er the Crossing" (No. 93) is peculiarly so; but "Sabbath has no end" (No. 89), "Hypocrite and Concubine" (No. 91),

"O shout away" (No. 92), and "Let God's saints come in" (No. 99), are all distinguished by odd intervals and a frequent use of chromatics. The songs from North Carolina are also very peculiar, although in a different way, and make one wish for more specimens from that region. Those from Tennessee and Florida are most like the music of the whites.

We had hoped to obtain enough secular songs to make a division by themselves; there are, however, so few of these that it has been decided to intersperse them with the spirituals under their respective States. They are highly characteristic, and will be found not the least interesting of the contents of this work.

It is, we repeat, already becoming difficult to obtain these songs. Even the "spirituals" are going out of use on the plantations, superseded by the new style of religious music, "closely imitated from the white people, which is solemn, dull and nasal, consisting in repeating two lines of a hymn and then singing it, and then two more, *ad infinitum*. They use for this sort of worship that one everlasting melody, which may be remembered by all persons familiar with Western and Southern camp-meetings, as applying equally well to long, short or common metre. This style of proceeding they evidently consider the more dignified style of the two, as being a closer imitation of white, genteel worship—having in it about as little soul as most stereotyped religious forms of well instructed congregations."*

---

* Mrs. H. B. Stowe, in *Watchman and Reflector*, April, 1867.

It remains to speak of points connected with the typography of the songs.

We have aimed to give all the characteristic variations which have come into our hands, whether as single notes or whole lines, or even longer passages; and of words as well as tunes. Many of these will be found very interesting and instructive. The variations in words are given as foot-notes—the word or group of words in the note, to be generally substituted for that which precedes the mark: and it may be observed, although it seems hardly necessary, that these variations are endless; such words as "member," "believer," "seeker," and all names, male and female, may be brought in wherever appropriate. We have not always given all the sets of words that we have received often they are improvised to such an extent that this would be almost impracticable. In Nos. 16, 17, 19, etc., we have given them very copiously, for illustration; in others we have omitted the least interesting ones. In spelling, we proposed to ourselves the rule well stated by Col. Higginson at the commencement of his collection: "The words will be here given, as nearly as possible, in the original dialect; and if the spelling seems sometimes inconsistent, or the misspelling insufficient, it is because I could get no nearer."

As the negroes have no part-singing, we have thought it best to print only the melody; what appears in some places as harmony is really variations in single notes. And, in general, a succession of such notes turned in the

same direction indicates a single longer variation. Words in a parenthesis, with small notes, (as "Brudder Sammy" in No. 21), are interjaculatory; it has not, however, been possible to maintain entire consistency in this matter. Sometimes, as "no man" and "O no man," in No. 14, interchangeable forms are put, for convenience sake, in different parts of the tune.

It may sometimes be a little difficult, for instance in Nos. 9, 10, 20 and 27, to determine precisely which part of the tune each verse belongs to; in these cases we have endeavored to indicate it as clearly as is in our power. However much latitude the reader may take in all such matters, he will hardly take more than the negroes themselves do. In repeating, it may be observed that the custom at Port Royal is to repeat the first part of the tune over and over, it may be a dozen times, before passing to the "turn," and then to do the same with that. In the Virginia songs, on the other hand, the chorus is usually sung twice after each verse—often the second time with some such interjaculatory expression as "I say now," "God say you must," as given in No. 99.

We had some thought of indicating with each the *tempo* of the different songs, but have concluded to print special directions for singing by themselves. It should be remarked, however, that the same tune varied in quickness on different occasions. "As the same songs," writes Miss McKim, "are sung at every sort of work, of course the *tempo* is not always alike. On the water, the

oars dip 'Poor Rosy' to an even *andante;* a stout boy and girl at the hominy mill will make the same 'Poor Rosy' fly, to keep up with the whirling stone; and in the evening, after the day's work is done, 'Heab'n shall-a be my home' peals up slowly and mournfully from the distant quarters. One woman, a respectable house-servant, who had lost all but one of her twenty-two children, said to me: 'Pshaw! don't har to dese yer chil'en, missee. Dey just rattles it off—dey don't know how for sing it. I likes 'Poor Rosy' better dan all de songs, but it can't be sung widout *a full heart and a troubled sperrit.*

The rests, by the way, do not indicate a cessation in the music, but only in part of the singers. They overlap in singing, as already described, in such a degree that at no time is there any complete pause. In "A House in Paradise" (No. 40) this overlapping is most marked.

It will be noticed that we have spoken chiefly of the negroes of the Port Royal islands, where most of our observations were made, and most of our materials collected. The remarks upon the dialect which follow have reference solely to these islands, and indeed almost exclusively to a few plantations at the northern end of St. Helena Island. They will, no doubt, apply in a greater or less degree to the entire region of the southeasterly slave States, but not to other portions of the South. It should also be understood that the corruptions and peculiarities here described are not universal, even here. There are

all grades, from the rudest field hands to mechanics and house-servants, who speak with a considerable degree of correctness, and perhaps few would be found so illiterate as to be guilty of them all.

Ordinary negro talk, such as we find in books, has very little resemblance to that of the negroes of Port Royal, who have been so isolated heretofore that they have almost formed a dialect of their own. Indeed, the different plantations have their own peculiarities, and adepts profess to be able to determine by the speech of a negro what part of an island he belongs to, or even, in some cases, his plantation. I can myself vouch for the marked peculiarities of speech of one plantation from which I had scholars, and which was hardly more than a mile distant from another which lacked these peculiarities. Songs, too, and, I suppose, customs, vary in the same way.

A stranger, upon first hearing these people talk, especially if there is a group of them in animated conversation, can hardly understand them better than if they spoke a foreign language, and might, indeed, easily suppose this to be the case. The strange words and pronunciations, and frequent abbreviations, disguise the familiar features of one's native tongue, while the rhythmical modulations, so characteristic of certain European languages, give it an utterly un-English sound. After six months' residence among them, there were scholars in my school, among the most constant in attendance, whom I could not understand at all, unless they happened to speak very slowly.

With these people the process of "phonetic decay" appears to have gone as far, perhaps, as is possible, and with it an extreme simplification of etymology and syntax. There is, of course, the usual softening of *th* and *v*, or *f*, into *d* and *b*; likewise a frequent interchange of *v* and *w*, as *veeds* and *vell* for *weeds* and *well*; *woices* and *punkin wine*, for *voices* and *pumpkin vine*. "De wile' (*vilest*) sinner may return" (No. 48). This last example illustrates also their constant habit of clipping words and syllables, as *lee' bro',* for *little brother; plänt'shun,* for *plantation.* The lengthening of short vowels is illustrated in both these (*a*, for instance, rarely has its short English sound). "Een (in) dat mornin' all day" (No. 56).

Strange words are less numerous in their *patois* than one would suppose, and, few as they are, most of them may be readily derived from English words. Besides the familiar *buckra*, and a few proper names, as Cuffy, Quash, and perhaps Cudjo, I only know of *churray* (spill), which may be "throw 'way;" *oona* or *ona,* "you" (both singular and plural, and used only for friends), as "Ona build a house in Paradise" (No. 40); and *aw*, a kind of expletive, equivalent to "to be sure," as, "Dat clot' cheap." "Cheap aw." "Dat Monday one lazy boy." "Lazy aw—I 'bleege to lick 'em."

Corruptions are more abundant. The most common of them are these: *Yearde* (hear), as in Nos. 3, etc. "Flora, did you see that cat?" "No ma'am, but I yearde him holler." "*Sh'um,*" a corruption of *see 'em,* applied (as *'em* is) to all genders and both numbers.

"Wan' to see how Beefut (Beaufort) stan'—nebber sh'um since my name Adam." *Huddy* (how-do?), pronounced *how-dy* by purists, is the common term of greeting, as in the song No. 20, "Tell my Jesus huddy O." "Bro' (brother) Quash sen' heap o' howdy." *Studdy,* (steady) is used to denote any continued or customary action. "He studdy 'buse an' cuss we," was the complaint entered by some little children against a large girl. "I studdy talk hard, but you no yearde me," was Rina's defence when I reproved her for not speaking loud enough. When we left, we were told that we must "studdy come back." Here, however, it seems to mean *steady. Titty* is used for mother or oldest sister; thus, Titty Ann was the name by which the children of our man-of-all work knew their mother, Ann. *Sic-a* or *sake-a,* possibly a condensation of *same* and *like.* "Him an' me grow up sic-a brudder an' sister." *Enty* is a curious corruption, I suppose of *ain't he,* used like our "Is that so?" in reply to a statement that surprises one. "Robert, you have n't written that very well." "Enty, sir?" John, it's going to rain to-day." "Enty, sir?" *Day-clean* is used for *day-break.* "Do, day-clean, for let me go see Miss Ha'yet; and de day wouldn't clean." *Sun-up* is also common. *Chu'* for "this" or "that there;" as "Wha' chu?" "See one knife chu?" *Say* is used very often, especially in singing, as a kind of expletive; "(Say) when you get to heaven (say) you 'member me." (No. 27.) "Ain't you know say cotton de-de?" In the last sentence "de-de" (accent on first syllable) means

"is there;"—the first *de*, a corruption of *does* for *is*, will be explained presently; the other is a very common form for *dere*, there.

I do not remember any other peculiar words, but several words used peculiarly. *Cuss* is used with great latitude, to denote any offensive language. "Him cuss me 'git out." "Ahvy (Abby) do cuss me," was the serious-sounding, but trifling accusation made by a little girl against her seat-mate. *Stan'* is a very common word, in the sense of *look.* "My back stan' like white man," was a boast which meant that it was not scarred with the lash. "Him stan' splendid, ma'am," of the sitting of a dress. I asked a group of boys one day the color of the sky. Nobody could tell me. Presently the father of one of them came by, and I told him their ignorance, repeating my question with the same result as before. He grinned: "Tom, how sky stan'?" "Blue," promptly shouted Tom. *Both* they seldom use; generally "all-two," or emphatically, "all-two boff togedder." *One* for *alone.* "Me one, and God," answered an old man in Charleston to the question whether he escaped alone from his plantation. "Gone home one in de dark," for alone. "Heab'n 'nuff for me one" (*i.e.*, I suppose, "for my part"), says one of their songs (No. 46.) *Talk* is one of their most common words, where we should use *speak* or *mean.* "Talk me, sir?" asks a boy who is not sure whether you mean him or his comrade. "Talk lick, sir? nuffin but lick," was the answer when I asked whether a particular master used to

whip his slaves. *Call* is used to express relationship; as, "he call him aunt." *Draw*, for receiving in any way — derived from the usage of drawing a specific amount of supplies at stated times. "Dey draw letter," was the remark when a mail arrived and was distributed among us whites. *Meet* is used in the sense of *find.* "I meet him here an' he remain wid me," was the cook's explanation when a missing chair was found in the kitchen. When I remarked upon the absurdity of some agricultural process—"I meet 'em so, an' my fader meet 'em so," was the sufficient answer. A grown man, laboring over the mysteries of simple addition, explained the gigantic answer he had got by "I meet two row, and I set down two." "I meet you dere, sir," said Miller frankly, when convinced in an argument. *Too much* is the common adverb for a high degree of a quality; "he bad *too* much" was the description of a hard master. *Gang*, for any large number; "a whole gang of slate-pencils." *Mash* in the sense of crush; "mammy mash 'em," when the goat had killed one of her kids by lying on it. *Sensibble* and *hab sense* are favorite expressions. A scholar would ask me to make him "sensibble" of a thing. "Nebber sh'um since I hab sense" (*i.e.*, since I was old enough to know). *Stantion* (substantial) was a favorite adjective at Coffin's Point. *Strain* is also a favorite word. "Dem boy strain me," explained Billy, when some younger boys were attempting to *base* him. "I don't want to give more nor fifty-five dollar for a horse," said Quash, "but if dey strain you, you may give fifty-six." "Dat tune *so* strainful," said Rose.

The letters *n, r* and *y* are used euphonically. "He de baddes' little gal from y'ere to n'Europe," said Bristol of his troublesome niece Venus; "ought to put him on a bar'l, an' den he fall 'sleep an' fall down an' hut heself, an' dat make him more sensibble." "He n'a comin', sir," was often said of a missing scholar. At first I took the *n* for a negative. I set Gib one day to picking out *E*'s from a box of letters. He could not distinguish *E* from *F*, and at last, discouraged with his repeated failures, explained, holding out an *F*, "dis y'ere stan' sic-a-r-*um*." (This looks like that.) It is suggested also that *d* is used in the same way, in "He d'a comin';" and *s*, in singing, for instance, "'Tis wells and good" (No. 25). So the vowel *a*; "De foxes have-a hole" (No. 2), "Heaven bell a-ring" (No. 27).

The most curious of all their linguistic peculiarities is perhaps the following. It is well known that the negroes in all parts of the South speak of their elders as "uncle" and "aunt,—"* from a feeling of politeness, I do not doubt; it seemed disrespectful to use the bare name, and from *Mr.* and *Mrs.* they were debarred. On the Sea Islands a similar feeling has led to the use of *cousin* towards their equals. Abbreviating this, after their fashion, they get *co'n* or *co'* (the vowel sound *u* as in *cousin*) as the common title when they speak of one another; as, C'Abram, Co' Robin, Co'n Emma, C'Isaac, Co'Bob. *Bro'* (brother) and *Si'* (sister) and even *T'* (Tit-

---

* In South Carolina "daddy" and "maum" are more common.

ty) are also often used in the same way; as, Bro' Paris, Si' Rachel, T' Jane. A friend insists that *Cudjo* is nothing but Co' Joe.

Where and *when* are hardly used, at least by the common class of negroes. The question "Where did you spill the milk?" was answered only with a stare; but "which way milk churray?" brought a ready response. "What side you stayin', sir?" was one of the first questions put to me. Luckily I had been initiated, and was able to answer it correctly.

There is probably no speech that has less inflection, or indeed less power of expressing grammatical relation in any way. It is perhaps not too strong to say that the field-hands make no distinction of gender, case, number, tense, or voice. The pronouns are to be sure distinguished more or less by the more intelligent among them, and all of these, unless perhaps *us*, are occasionally heard. *She* is rare; *her* still more so; *him* being commonly used for the third person singular of all cases and genders; *'em*, if my memory serves me rightly, only for the objective case, but for all genders and both numbers. *He*, or *'e*, is, I should think, most common as possessive. "Him lick we" might mean a girl as well as a boy. Thus *we* is distinguished from *I* or *me*, and *dey* or *dem* from *him* or *dat*; and these are, I think, the only distinctions made in number. "Dat cow," is singular, "dem cow" plural; "Sandy hat" would mean indifferently Sandy's hat or hats; "nigger-house" means the collection of negro-houses, and is, I suppose, really a plural.

I do not know that I ever heard a real possessive case, but they have begun to develop one of their own, which is a very curious illustration of the way inflectional forms grow up. If they wish to make the fact of possession at all emphatic or distinct, they use the word "own." Thus, they will say "Mosey house," but if asked whose house that is, the answer is "Mosey own." "Co' Molsy y'own" was the odd reply made by Mylie to the question whose child she was carrying. Literally translated, this is "Molsy's;" *Co'* is title, *y* euphonic. An officer of a colored regiment standing by me when the answer was made—himself born a slave—confessed that it was mere gibberish to him. No doubt this custom would in time develop a regular inflectional possessive; but the establishment of schools will soon root up all these original growths.

Very commonly, in verbs which have strong conjugations, the forms of the past tense are used for the present; "What make you leff we?" "I tuk dem brudder" (No. 30). Past time is expressed by *been*, and less commonly *done*. "I been kep him home two day," was the explanation given for a daughter's absence from school. "I done pit my crap in de groun'." Present time is made definite by the auxiliary *do* or *da*, as in the refrains "Bell da ring," "Jericho da worry me." (Nos. 46, 47). "Bubber (brother) da hoe he tater." So *did* occasionally: "Nat did cuss me," complained one boy of another. It is too much to say that the verbs have no inflections, but it is true that these have nearly disap-

peared. Ask a boy where he is going, and the answer is "gwine crick for ketch crab" (going into the creek to catch crabs); ask another where the missing boy is, and the answer is the same, with *gone* instead of *gwine*. The hopeless confusion between auxiliaries is sometimes very entertaining: as "de-de," "ain't you know?" "I didn't been." "De Lord is perwide" (No. 2). "You'd better pray, de worl' da [is] gwine" (No. 14). "My stomach been-a da hut me."

Some of these sentences illustrate two other peculiarities—the omission of auxiliaries and other small words, and the use of *for* as the sign of the infinitive. "Unky Taff call Co' Flora for drop tater." "Good for hold comb" was the wisest answer found to the teacher's question what their ears were good for. "Co' Benah wan' Mr.—for tuk 'em down," was Gib's whispered comment when the stubborn Venus refused to step down from a bench. After school the two were discovered at fisticuffs, and on being called to account—"dat same Benah dah knock me," said Gib, while Venus retorted with "Gib cuss me in school."

It is owing to this habit of dropping auxiliaries that the passive is rarely if ever indicated. You ask a man's name, and are answered, "Ole man call John." "Him mix wid him own fat," was the description given of a paste made of bruised ground-nuts, the oil of the nut furnishing moisture. "I can't certain," "The door didn't fasten," "The bag won't full," "Dey frighten in de dark," are illustrations of every-day usage.

Proper names furnish many curious illustrations of the corruption in pronunciation. Many of them are impossible to explain, and it is still only a surmise that *Finnick* is derived from *Phœnix*, and *Wyna* from *Malvina* (the first syllable being dropped, as in '*Nelius* for *Cornelius*, and '*Rullus* for *Marullus*.) *Hacless* is unquestionably *Hercules*, and *Sack* no doubt *Psyche*; *Strappan* is supposed to be *Strephon*. All these are common names on the Sea Islands. Names of trades, as *Miller*, *Butcher*, are not uncommon. One name that I heard of, but did not myself meet with, was *After-dark*, so called because he was so black that "you can't sh'um 'fo' day-clean."

In conclusion, some actual specimens of talk, illustrating the various points spoken of, may not be without interest. A scene at the opening of school :*

"Charles, why did n't you come to school earlier ?" "A-could n't come *soon* to-day, sir ; de boss he sheer out clo' dis mornin'." "What did he give you ?" "Me, sir ? I ain't *git ;* de boss he de baddest buckra ebber a-see. De morest part ob de mens dey git heaps o' clo'—more'n 'nuff ; 'n I ain't git nuffin." "Were any other children there ?" "Plenty chil'n, sir. All de chil'n dah fo' sun-up." "January, you have n't brought your book." "I *is*, sir ; sh'um here, sir ?" "Where is Juno ?" "I ain't

---

* It is proper to state that most of the materials for this scene were furnished by Mr. Arthur Sumner, which accounts for the similarity of certain of the expressions to those in the dialogue given in the September number of the Boston *Freedman's Record*.

know where he gone, sir." "Where is Sam ?" "He didn't been here." "Where is the little boy, John ?" "He pick up he foot and run." A new scholar is brought : "Good mornin', maussa ; I bring dis same chile to school, sir : *do* don't let 'em stay arter school done. Here you, gal, stan' up an' say howdy to de genlmn. Do maussa lash 'em well ef he don't larn he lesson." "Where's your book, Tom ?" "Dunno, sir. Some*body* mus' a tief 'em." "Where's your brother?" "Sh'um dar ? wid bof he han' in he pocket ?" "Billy, have you done your sum ?" "Yes, sir, I out 'em." "Where's Polly ?" "Polly de-de." Taffy comes up. "Please, sir, make me sensibble of dat word—I want to ketch 'em werry bad, sir, werry bad." Hacless begins to read. He spells in a loud whisper, "g-o ; g-o ; g-o—can't fetch dat word, sir, nohow."

The first day Gib appeared in school I asked him whether he could read, and received a prompt answer in the affirmative. So, turning to the first page of Willson's Primer, I told him to read. The sentence was "I am on," or something of that sort, opposite a picture of a boy on a rocking-horse. Gib attacked it with great volubility, "h-r-s-e, horse. De boy is on top ob de horse"—adding some remarks about a chair in the background. His eye then fell on a picture of an eagle, and without pausing he went on, "De raben is big bird." Next he passed to a lion on the opposite page, "D-o-g, dog ;" but just then a cut above, representing a man and an ox, proved too strong for him, and he proceeded

to give a detailed history of the man and the cow. When this was completed, he took up a picture of a boy with a paper soldiers' cap and a sword. "Dis man hab sword ; he tuk 'e sword an' cut 'e troat." Here I checked him, and found, as may be expected, that he did not know a single letter.

A scene at a government auction : Henry and Titus are rivals, bidding for a piece of "secesh" furniture. Titus begins with six dollars. "Well, Titus, I won't strain you—eight." "Seven," says Titus. "Ten," says Henry. "Twelve," says Titus. "And den," said our informant, "Henry bid fourteen an' tuk 'em for fifteen."

One day when we returned from a row on the creek, to make a call, Dick met us with his face on a grin : "You seen him ? you seen Miss T ? *I* seen him. I tole him you gone wid intention call on she, but de boat didn't ready in time. He cotch you at Mr. H., on'y de horse bodder him at de gate." One of the boys came to me one day with the complaint, " Dem Ma' B. Fripp chil'n fin' one we book," *i. e.*, those children from Mr. T. B. Fripp's have found one of our books. "'E nebber crack 'e bret," *i. e.*, say a word. "What make you don't ?" "Mr. P. didn't must." "I don't know what make I didn't answer." "How do you do to-day ?" "Stirrin ;" "spared," "standin';" "out o' bed," (never "very well.") Or, of a friend, "He feel a lee better'n he been, ma'am."

"Arter we done chaw all de hard bones and swallow all de bitter pills," was part of a benediction ; and the

prayer at a "praise-meeting" asked "dat all de white xxxvi bredren an' sister what jine praise wid we to-night might be bound up in de belly-band ob faith." At a funeral in a colored regiment : "One box o' dead meat gone to de grave to-day—who gwine to-morrow ? Young man, who walk so stiff—ebery step he take seem like he say, 'Look out dah, groun', I da comin'." The following is Strappan's view of Love. "Arter you lub, you lub, you know, boss. You can't broke lub. Man can't broke lub. Lub stan'—'e ain't gwine broke. Man hab to be berry smart for broke lub. Lub is a ting stan' jus' like tar ; arter he stick, he stick, he ain't gwine move. He can't move less dan you burn him. Hab to kill all two arter he lub 'fo' you broke lub."

It would be an interesting, and perhaps not very difficult inquiry, to determine how far the peculiarities of speech of the South Carolina negroes result from the large Huguenot element in the settlement of that State. It would require, however, a more exact acquaintance than I possess with the dialects of other portions of the South, to form a judgment of any value upon this point. Meanwhile, I will say only that two usages have struck me as possibly arising from this source, the habitual lengthening of vowel sounds, and the pronunciation of *Maussa*, which may easily have been derived from *Monsieur*. After all, traces of Huguenot influence should by right be found among the whites, even more than the blacks.

[W. F. A.]

It remains for the Editors to acknowledge the aid they have received in making this compilation. To Col. T. W. Higginson, above all others, they are indebted for friendly encouragement and for direct and indirect contributions to their original stock of songs. From first to last he has manifested the kindest interest in their undertaking, constantly suggesting the names of persons likely to afford them information, and improving every opportunity to procure them material. As soon as his own valuable collection had appeared in the *Atlantic Monthly*, he freely made it over to them with a liberality which was promptly confirmed by his publishers, Messrs. Ticknor & Fields. It is but little to say that without his co-operation this *Lyra Africana* would have lacked greatly of its present completeness and worth. Through him we have profited by the cheerful assistance of Mrs. Charles J. Bowen, Lieut.-Colonel C. T. Trowbridge, Capt. James S. Rogers, Rev. Horace James, Capt. Geo. S. Barton, Miss Lucy Gibbons, Mr. William A. Baker, Mr. T. E. Ruggles, and Mr. James Schouler. Our thanks are also due for contributions, of which we have availed ourselves, to Dr. William A. Hammond, Mr. Geo. H. Allan, Lt.-Col. Wm. Lee Apthorp, Mr. Kane O'Donnel, Mr. E. J. Snow, Miss Charlotte L. Forten, Miss Laura M. Towne, and Miss Ellen Murray; and for criticisms, suggestions, communications, and unused but not unappreciated contributions, to Mr. John R. Dennett, Miss Annie Mitchell, Mr. Reuben Tomlinson, Mr. Arthur Sumner, Mr. N. C. Dennett, Miss Mary Ellen Peirce, Maj.-Gen. Wager Swayne, Miss Maria W. Benton, Prof. J. Silsby, Rev. John L. McKim, Mr. Albert Griffin, Mr. A. S. Jenks, Mr. E. H. Hawkes, Rev. H. C. Trumbull, Rev. J. K. Hosmer, Rev. F. N. Knapp, Brev. Maj.-Gen. Truman Seymour, Maj.-Gen. James H. Wilson, Mr. J. H. Palmer, and others; and, finally, to the editors of various newspapers who gratuitously announced the forthcoming volume.

Conscious of many imperfections in this, the result of not inconsiderable joint labor for nearly a year, the Editors submit it, nevertheless, to the public judgment, in the belief that it will be pronounced deserving of even greater pains and of permanent preservation.

William Francis Allen,
Charles Pickard Ware,
Lucy McKim Garrison.

Roll, Jordan, Roll

1. My brud-der sit-tin' on de tree of life, An' he year-de when Jor-dan roll; _____ Roll, Jor-dan, roll, Jor-dan roll, Jor-dan roll! O march de an-gel, march, O march de an-gel, march; O my soul, a-rise in

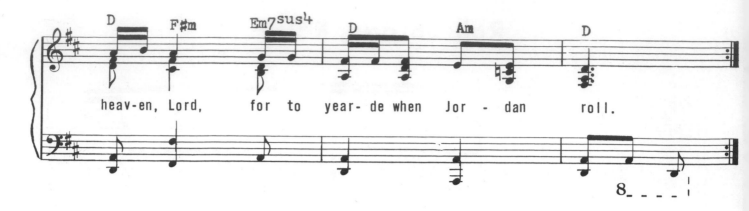

heav-en, Lord, for to year- de when Jor - dan roll.

2 Little chil'en, learn to fear de Lord,
   And let your days be long;
      Roll, Jordan, *etc.*

3 O let no false nor spiteful word
   Be found upon your tongue;
      Roll, Jordan, *(etc.)*

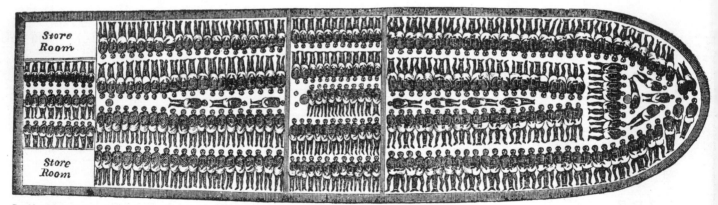

Sectional drawing of the deck of a slave ship, 1808

Jehovah, Hallelujah

Je - ho - viah, hal - le - lu- jah, de Lord is per -
                                    (will pro -

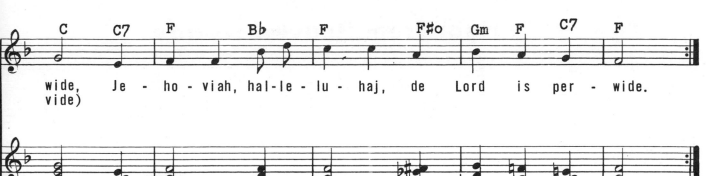

wide, Je - ho - viah, hal-le - lu - haj, de Lord is per - wide.
vide)

De fox - es have a hole, an' de bird -ies have a nest, de

Son of man He __ dun- no where to lay de wea - ry head.

I Hear From Heaven To-day

Hur-ry on, my wea-ry soul, And I

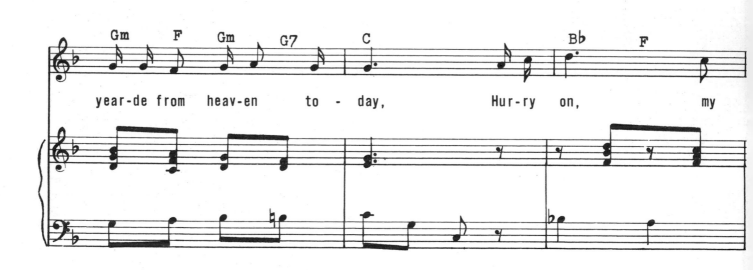

year-de from heav-en to - day, Hur-ry on, my

wea-ry soul, And I year-de from heav-en to - day. Hur-ry

day. 1. My __ sin is for-giv-en and my soul set free, And I year-de from heav-en to - day, My sin is for-giv-en, and my soul set free, And I year-de from heav-en to - day.

2 A baby born in Bethlehem,
   And I yearde, *etc.*
3 De trumpet sound in de oder bright land,
4 My name is called and I must go.
5 De bell is a-ringin' in de oder bright
                                   world.

Blow Your Trumpet, Gabriel

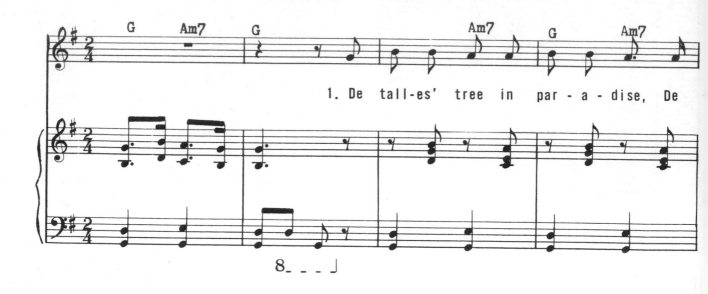

1. De tall-es' tree in par - a - dise, De

Chris - tian call de tree of life; And I hope dat trump might

blow me home to de new Je- ru - sa - lem.

Blow your trum-pet. Ga-briel, Blow loud-er, loud-er, And I

hope dat trump might blow me home to de new Je-ru-sa-lem.

2 Paul and Silas, bound in jail,
Sing God's praise both night and day;
And I hope, *etc.*

Alternate version:

Paul and Si-las, bound in jail, Chris-tians pray both night and day, And I

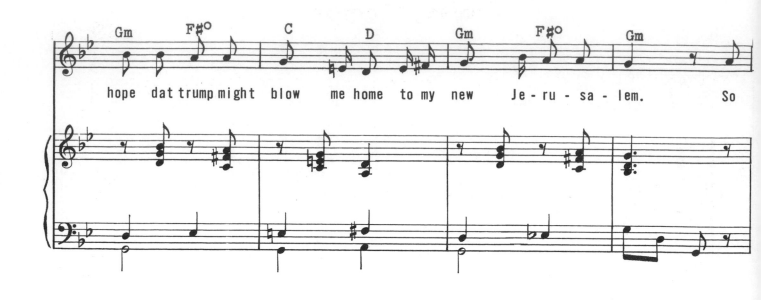

hope dat trump might blow me home to my new Je-ru-sa-lem. So

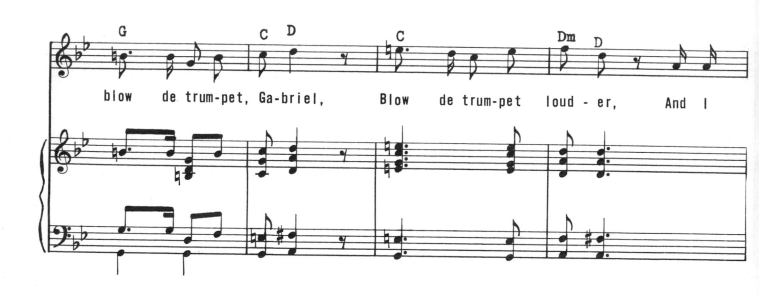

blow de trum-pet, Ga-briel, Blow de trum-pet loud-er, And I

D. S. (first version)

hope dat trump might blow me home, to my new Je-ru-sa-lem.

Praise, Member

Praise, mem - ber, praise ___ God, I praise my God un - til I die. Praise, mem - ber, praise ___ God, And reach de heav-en-ly home. home. 1. O ___ Jor-dan's bank is a

good old bank, And I hain't but one more riv-er to cross I

want some val-iant sol - dier to help me bear de cross. cross.

2 O soldier's is a good old fight
   And I hain't, *etc.*

3 O I look to de East, and I look to de
                                    West.

4 O I wheel to de right, and I wheel
                            to de left.

Wrestle On, Jacob

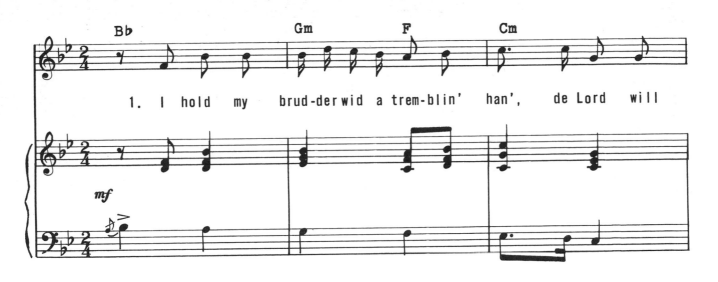

1. I hold my brud-der wid a trem-blin' han', de Lord will

bless my soul. Wras - tl' on, Ja - cob, Ja - cob,

day is a - break - in', Wras - tl' on,

Ja - cob, Oh he would not let him go.

2 I will not let you go, my Lord.
3 Fisherman Peter out to sea.
4 He cast all night and he cast all day.
5 He catch no fish but he catch some soul.
6 Jacob hang from a tremblin' limb.

The Lonesome Valley

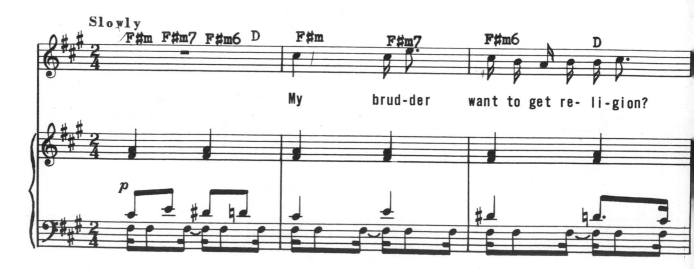

My brud-der want to get re- li-gion?

Go down in de lone-some val-ley. 1. Go down in de lone-some
val-ley, _____ Go down in de lone-some val-ley, my Lord, Go
down in de lone-some val - ley to meet my Je-sus dere. dere.

2   O feed on milk and honey.
3   O John he write de letter.
4   And Mary and Marta read 'em.

I Can't Stay Behind

Room e-nough, room e-nough, I can't stay be-hind.

2 I been all around, I been all around.
Been all around de heaven, my Lord.

3 I'm searched every room - in de heaven,
my Lord.

4 De angels singin' - all around de trone.

5 My Fader call - and I must go.

6 Sto-back, member; sto-back, member.

Slaves in Jackson Square, New Orleans (ca. 1857)

Poor Rosy

1. Poor Ro-sy, poor __ gal, Poor Ro-sy, poor __ gal,

2   Got hard trial in my way *(three times)*
     Heav'n shall-a be my home.
    O when I talk I talk wid God *(twice)*
     Heav'n shall-a be my home.

3   I dunno what de people want to me *(3 times)*
     Heav'n shall-a be my home.

The Trouble Of The World

1. I want to be my Fa-der's chil'-en, I want to be my Fa-der's chil'-en, I want to be my fa-der's chil'-en, Roll, Jor-dan, roll. O say, ain't you done wid de trou-ble ob de world, Ah _____ Trou-ble ob de world, Ah!

Say, ain't you done wid de trou-ble ob de world, Ah! Roll, Jor-dan, roll.

2. I ask de Lord how long I hold 'em
   (three times)
   Hold 'em to de end.
3. My sins so heavy, I can't get along, Ah!
   (etc.)
4. I cast my sins in de middle of de sea, Ah!
   (etc.)

Sojourner Truth

There's A Meeting Here To-night

I I take my text in Mat-tew and by de Rev-e-la-tion, I know you by your gar-ment, Dere's a meet-ing here to-night.

Dere's a meet-ing here to - night (Brud-der To-ny) Dere's a meet- ing here to - night (Sis-ter Re - na) Dere's a meet - ing here to - night, I hope to meet a - gain. I see brud-der Mo- ses yon- der and I think I ought to kmow him, For I know him by his gar-ments, He's a bless-ing here to-night. He's a

bless-ing here to - night, He's a bless-ing here to-night And I

think I ought to know him, He's a bless-ing here to - night.

Hold Your Light

What make ole Sa - tan da fol - low me so? Sa - tan ain't not-tin' at all for to do wid

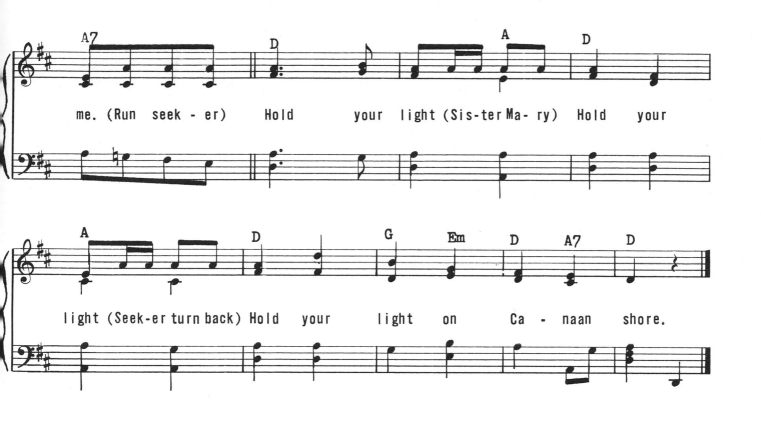

me. (Run seek - er) Hold your light (Sis-ter Ma- ry) Hold your

light (Seek-er turn back) Hold your light on Ca - naan shore.

Happy Morning

Weep no more, Mar - ta, Weep no more, Ma - ry, Je - sus

rise from de dead hap - py morn - - ing.

Glo-rious morn - - ing, glo-rious morn - - ing, My Sa-viour rise from de dead hap-py morn - - ing.

No Man Can Hinder Me

Walk in, kind Sav - iour, No man can hin-der me, Walk in, sweet Je - sus, No man can hin-der me.

2. See what won-der Je-sus done, O no man can hin - der me.

See what won - der Je - sus done, O no man can hin - der me.

O no man, no man, no man can hin - der me, O

no man, no man, no man can hin der me.

3. Jesus make de dumb to speak.
4. Jesus make de cripple walk.
5. Jesus give de blind his sight.
6. Jesus do most anything.
7. Rise, poor Lajarush, from de tomb.
8. Satan ride an iron-gray horse.
9. King Jesus ride a milk-white horse.

Lord, Remember Me

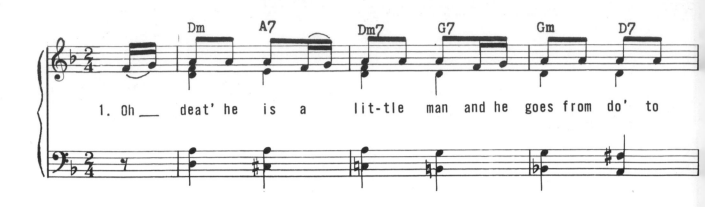

1. Oh __ deat' he is a lit-tle man and he goes from do' to

do' He kill some souls and he wound - ed some and he

lef' some souls to pray. Oh Lord, re-mem - ber

me, Do Lord re-mem - ber me, Re - mem-ber me as de

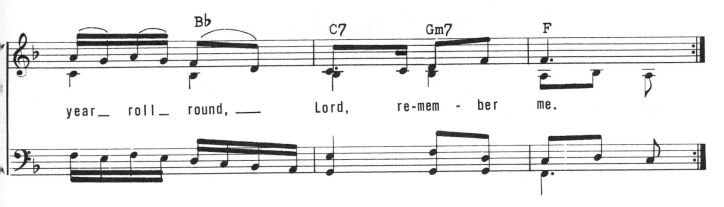

year_ roll_ round, ___ Lord, re-mem - ber me.

2 I want to die like-a Jesus die
   And He die wid a free good will,
   I lay out in de grave and I stretched
                              out de arms,
       Do, Lord remember me.

Not Weary Yet

O me no wea-ry yet, O ___ me no wea-ry yet. 1. I

have a wit-ness in my heart, O me no wea-ry yet (Brud-der Tony) yet.

(Sis-ter Ma-ry)

2. Since I been in de field to fight.   5. Ole Satan toss a ball at me.
3. I have a heaven to maintain.   6. Him tink de ball would hit my soul.
4. De bond of faith are on my soul.   7. De ball for hell and I for heaven.

Religion So Sweet

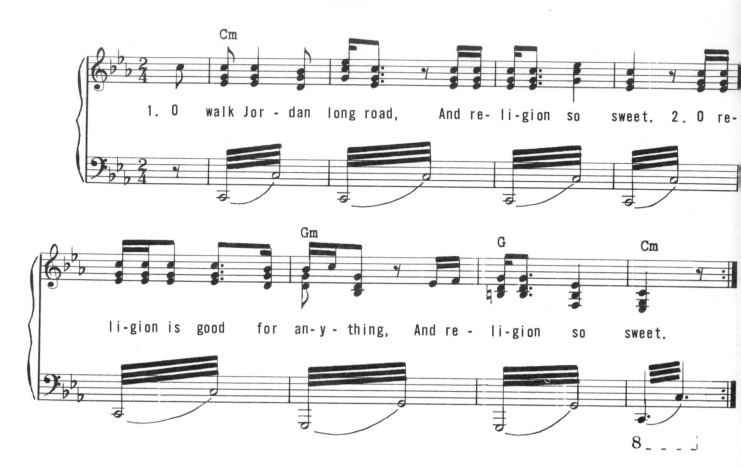

1. O walk Jor - dan long road, And re- li - gion so sweet. 2. O re-
li -gion is good for an-y-thing, And re - li -gion so sweet.

3   Religion make you happy.
4   Religion gib me patience.
5   O member, get religion.
6   I long time been a-huntin'
7   I seekin' for my fortune.
8   O I gwine to meet my Saviour.
9   Gwine to tell Him 'bout my trials.
10   Dey call me boastin' member.
11   Dey call me turnback Christian.
12   Dey call me 'struction maker.
13   But I don't care what dey call me.
14   Lord, trial 'longs to a Christian.
15   O tell me 'bout religion.
16   I weep for Mary and Marta.
17   I seek my Lord and I find Him.

Hunting For The Lord

Hunt till you find Him, Hal-le-lu-jah, And a-hunt-in' for de Lord, Till you find Him, Hal-le-lu-jah, And a-hunt-in' for de Lord.

Go In The Wilderness

I wait up-on de Lord, I wait up-on de Lord, I wait up-on de Lord, my God, who

take a-way de sin of de world. I world. If you

want to find Je - sus, go in de wil-der-ness, go in de wil-der-ness,

go in de wil-der-ness, Mourn- in', Brud- der, go in de wil-der-ness, I

wait up - on de Lord. If you Lord.

3. You want to be a Christian
4. You want to get religion
5. If you spec' to be connected
6. O weepin' Mary
7. 'Flicted sister
8. Say, ain't you a member?
9. Half-done Christian
10. Come, backslider
11. Babtist member
12. O seek, brudder Bristol
13. Jesus a-waitin' to meet you in
    de wilderness

Tell My Jesus "Morning"

1. In de morn-in' when I rise, Tell my Je - sus hud-dy oh, I wash my hands in de morn-in' glo-ry, Tell my Je - sus hud-dy oh.

2. Pray, To- ny, pray, boy, you got de or - der.

3 Mornin', Hester, mornin', gal,
   Tell my Jesus, *etc.*

4 Say, brudder Sammy, you got de order,
   Tell my Jesus, *etc.*

5 You got de order, and I got de order.

The Graveyard

Brud-der Sam-my 1. Who gwine to lay dis bod-y mem - ber

O shout glo - ry, And a - who gwine to lay dis bod-y, Oh

Ring Je-ru - sa - lem. 2. O call all de mem-ber to de grave-yard mem-ber

3   O graveyard, ought to know me.
4   O grass grow in de graveyard.
5   I reel and I rock in de graveyard.
6   O I walk and I toss wid Jesus.
7   My mudder reel and a-toss wid de fever.
8   I have a grandmudder in de graveyard.
9   O when d'ye tink I find them?
10   I find 'em, Lord, in de graveyard.
11   I wheel and I rock, and I gwine home.
12   O 'peat dat story over.

John, John, Of The Holy Order

John, John of the Ho- ly Or- der, Sit-tin' on de gold- en or - - der, John, John wid de Ho- ly Or- der, Sit-tin' on de gold- en or - der. John, John wid de Ho- ly or- der, Sit-tin' on de gold- en or - der, To view de prom- ised land, O Lord, I weep, I mourn, Why

don't you move so slow? I'm a-hunt-in' for some guard-ian an-gel gone a-long be-fore. Ma-ry and Mar-ta feed my lamb, feed my lamb, feed my lamb, Si-mon, Pe-ter feed my Lamb, a-sit-tin' on de gold-en or-der.

Cotton Picking on a Plantation

I Saw The Beam In My Sister's Eye

I saw de beam in my sis-ter's eye, Can't saw de beam in mine. You'd bet-ter lef' your sis-ter door, Go keep your own door clean.

2 And I had a mighty battle like-a
                     Jacob and de angel,
    Jacob, time of old;
    I didn't 'tend to lef' 'em go
    Till Jesus bless my soul.

3 And blessèd me, and blessèd my,
    And blessèd all my soul;
    I didn't 'tend to lef' 'em go
    Till Jesus bless my soul.

Hunting For A City

I am hunt-in' for a cit-y, to __ stay a __ while, I am

hunt-in' for a cit-y, to __ stay a while. I am hunt-in' for a cit-y, __ to

stay a __ while, O be-liev-er, got a home at __ last.

Gwine Follow

Tit-ty Ma-ry, you know I gwine fol-low, I gwine fol-low, gwine

fol-low, Brud-der Wil-liam, you know I gwine to fol-low for to

do my fa-der will. 'Tis well and good I'm a-com-in' here to-night, I'm a-com-in' here to-night, I'm a-com-in' here to-night, 'Tis well and good I'm a-com-in' here to-night, for to do my fa-der will.

Fugitive Slaves fleeing from Cambridge, Maryland, to Delaware.

Lay This Body Down

1. O grave-yard, — O grave-yard, — I'm walk-in' troo de grave-yard, — Lay dis bo-dy down.

2. I know moonlight, I know starlight,
I'm walkin' troo de starlight;
Lay dis body down.

Alternate Version:

I know moon-light, I know star-light; I lay dis bo-dy down.

2 I walk in de moonlight, I walk in de
starlight;
I lay dis body down.

3 I know de graveyard, I know de graveyard,
When I lay dis body down.

4 I walk in de graveyard, I walk troo
de graveyard,
To lay, (etc.)

5 I lay in de grave an' stretch out
my arms;
I lay, (etc.)

6 I go to de judgment in de evenin' of de
day
When I lay, (etc.)

7 And my soul an' your soul will meet
in de day
When I lay, (etc.)

Heaven Bell A-Ring

1. My Lord, my Lord, what shall I do? And a-heav-'n bell a-ring and praise God.

My Lord, my Lord, what shall I do? And a-heav-'n bell a-ring and praise God.

2   What shall I do for a hiding place?
       And a-heav'n, *etc.*

3   I run to de sea, but de sea run dry.

4   I run to de gate, but de gate shut fast.

5   No hiding place for sinner dere.

6   Say you when you get to heaven, say
       you 'member me.

7   Remember me, poor fallen soul.

8   Say when you get to heaven, say your
       work shall prove.

9   Your righteous Lord shall prove 'em well.

10   Your righteous Lord shall find you out.

11   He cast out none that come by faith.

12   You look to de Lord wid a tender heart.

13   I wonder where poor Monday dere.

14   For I am gone and sent to hell.

15   We must harkee what de wordly say.

16   Say Christmas come but once a year.

17   Say Sunday come but once a week.

Jine 'em

On Sun-day morn-in' I seek my Lord, Jine 'em, jine 'em, oh! Oh

jine 'em, be-liev-er, jine 'em so; Jine 'em, jine 'em, oh!

Rain Fall And Wet Becca Lawton

Rain fall and wet Bec-ca Law - ton, Oh, _____

Rain fall and wet Bec-ca Law - ton, Oh! Brud-der cry ho - ly.

Been back ho - ly, I must come slow-ly, Oh, Brud-der cry ho - ly.

2 Do, Becca Lawton, come to me yonder.
3 Say, brudder Tony, what shall I do now?
4 Beat back holy, and rock salvation.

Bound To Go

1. I build my house up - on de rock, O yes

Lord, No wind, no storm can blow 'em down, O yes Lord.

March on, mem-ber bound to go, Bound to de fer-ry, bound to go.

Left St. He-le-na bound to go, Brud-der, fare you well.

2 I build my home on shiftin' sand,
   De first wind come he blow him down.

3 I am not like de foolish man,
   He build his house upon de sand.

4 One mornin' as I was walkin' along,
   I saw de berries a-hanging down.

5 I pick de berries and I suck de juice,
   He sweeter dan de honey comb.

6 I took dem brudder, two by two,
   I took dem sister, tree by tree.

Auction at Richmond.

58

Michael Row The Boat Ashore

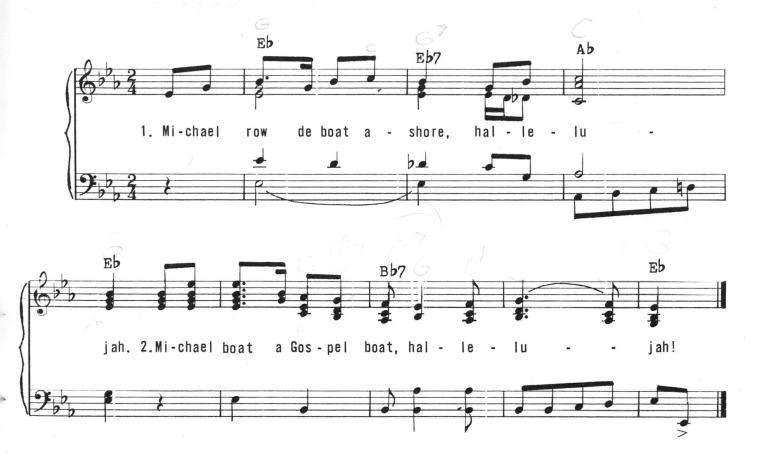

3 I wonder where my mudder den. (there)	13 Jesus stand on t' oder side.
4 See my mudder on de rock gwine home.	14 I wonder if my maussa deh.
5 On de rock gwine home in Jesus' home.	15 My fader gone to unknown land.
6 Michael boat a music boat	16 O de Lord he plant his garden deh.
7 Gabriel blow de trumpet horn.	17 He raise de fruit for you to eat.
8 O you mind your boastin' talk.	18 He dat eat shall neber die.
9 Boastin' talk will sink your soul.	19 When de riber overflow.
10 Brudder, lend a helpin' hand.	20 O poor sinner, how you land?
11 Sister, help for trim dat boat.	21 Riber run and darkness comin'.
12 Jordan stream is wide and deep.	22 Sinner run to save your soul.

Additional lyrics:

Michael haul de boat ashore.
Then you'll hear the horn they blow.
Then you'll hear the trumpet sound.
Trumpet sound the world around.
Trumpet sound for rich and poor.
Trumpet sound the jubilee.
Trumpet sound for you and me.

Sail, O Believer

Sail, O be - liev-er, sail, sail o - ver yon - der.

Sail, O my brud-der, sail, sail o - ver yon - der.

Harriet Beecher Stowe

Frederick Douglass

Rock O' Jubilee

1. O Rock o' Ju - bi - lee, poor fall- en soul, O Lord de

Rock o' Ju - bi - lee. 2. O Rock o' Ju - bi - lee, And I

rock 'em all a - bout, O Lord, de Rock o' Ju - bi - lee.

3 Stand back, Satan, let me come by.
4 O come, titty Katy, let me go.
5 I have no time for stay at home.
6 My fader door wide open now.
7 Mary, girl, you know my name.
8 Look dis way an' you look dat way.
9 De wind blow East, he blow from Jesus.

Stars Begin To Fall

I tink I hear my brud- der say, Call de na-tion great and small; I

look-ee on de God's right hand _ when de stars be-gin to fall.

Oh   what a mourn-in' (sis-ter), Oh   what a mourn-in' (brud-der),

Oh   what a mourn-in'; when de stars be-gin to fall.

Slaves in the Rice Fields

King Emanuel

1. O my King E-ma-nu-el, My E-ma-nu-el a-bove, sing glo-ry to my King E-ma-nu-el.

2. If you walk de gold-en street and you join de gold-en band, Sing glo-ry be to my King E-ma-nu-el.

3 If you touch one string, den de whole
heaven ring.

4 O de great cherubim, O de cherubim
above.

5 O believer, ain't you glad dat your
soul is converted?

Satan's Camp A-Fire

Fi-er, my Sav-iour, fi-er, _____ Sa-tan's camp a - fire;

Fi-er, be-liev-er, fi - er, _____ Sa-tan's camp a-fire.

John Brown

Negro Soldier (Civil War)

Give Up The World

De sun give a light in de heav-en all round, De

Sugar Plantation

Slave Quarters

Jesus On The Water-Side

Heav-en bell a-ring, I know de road, Heav-en bell a-ring, I know de road, Heav-en bell a-ring, I know de road, Je-sus sit-tin' on de wa-ter side. Do come a-long, do let us go, do come a-long, do let us go, Do come a-long, do

let us go, ___ Je - sus sit-tin' on de wa - ter side.

I Wish I Been Dere

My mud-der you fol-low Je - sus, My sis-ter you fol - low Je - sus, My brud-der you fol-low Je-sus To fight un-til I die.

I wish I been yon-der dere to climb Ja - cob's lad - der, I

wish I been yon - der dere to wear de star - ry crown.

Build A House In Paradise

My Fa - der build a house

My brud - der build a house in Par - a - dise, O - na build a house in

Par - a - dise. Par - a - dise. Build it wid - out a

ham - mer and a nail, Build it wid - out a ham - mer or a nail.

I Know When I'm Going Home

Old Sa - tan told me to my face, O yes Lord, De God I seek I nev-er find, O yes Lord. True be - liev-er, I know when I gwine home, True be - liev-er, I know when I gwine home, True be - liev-er, I know when I gwine home, I been a - fraid to die.

I'm A-Trouble In De Mind

I am a-trou-ble in de mind, O I am a-

trou-ble in de mind; I ask my Lord what shall I do,

I am a-trou-ble in de mind. I'm a - trou-ble in de mind,

what you doubt for? I'm a - trou-ble in de mind. _____

Travel On

Archangel Open The Door

I ax all dem brud-der roun', brud-der why can't you pray for

me? I ax all dem brud-der roun', brud-der why

can't you pray for me? 1. I'm gwine to my heav-en, I'm

gwine home, Arch-an-gel o-pen de door; I'm

gwine to my heav-en I'm gwine home,   Arch - an - gel o-pen de door.

2   Brudder, tuk off your knapsack,
                    I'm gwine home;
         Archangel open de door.

Cotton Field

My Body Rock 'long Fever

1. Wai', my brud-der, bet-ter true be-lieve,   Bet-ter true be-long time

get o-ver cross-es; Wai', my sis-ter, Bet-ter true be-lieve, An' 'e

get up to heav-en at last. O my bo - dy rock 'long fe - ver O! ___

___ wid a pain in 'e head! I wish I been to de King-dom, to

sit a-long side o' my Lord. O my bo - dy's racked wid de

fe - ve - er, My head racked wid de pain I hab, I wish I was in de

King-do - om, A - set-tin' on de side ob de Lord. _____

2   By de help ob de Lord we rise up again,
     O de Lord He comfort de sinner;
     By de help ob de Lord we rise up again,
     An' we'll get to heaben at last.

Bell Da Ring

I know,   mem- ber,   know, Lord,   I   know   I yed- de   de

bell   da   ring.   1.Want to go   to meet - ing,   Bell   da   ring,

Want to go to meet - ing,   Bell   da   ring.   ring.   2.(Say) Road so storm-y,

Bell   da   ring, (Say)   Road   so   storm - y,   Bell   da   ring.

3   I can't get to meetin'.
4   De church mos' ober.
5   De heaven-bell a heaven-bell.
6   De heaven-bell I gwine home.
7   I shout for de heaven-bell.
8   Heaven 'nough for me one.
9   (Brudder) hain't you a member?
10 Do my brudder, O yes, member.

11 You can't get to heaben.
12 If you want to get to heaben.
13 You had better follow Jesus.
14 O yes, my Jesus, yes, I member.
15 O come in, Christians.
16 For the gates are all shut.
17 And you can't get to heaben.

Pray All De Member

4   Jericho, Jericho
5   I been to Jerusalem.
6   Patrol aroun' me.
7   Tank God He no ketch me.
8   Went to de meetin'.

9   Met brudder Hacless (Hercules)
10 Wha' d'ye tink he tell me?
11 Tell me for to turn back.
12 Jump along Jericho.

Turn, Sinner, Turn O!

1. Turn, sin - ner, turn to - day, turn, sin - ner, turn O!
2. Turn, O sin - ner, de world da gwine, turn, sin - ner, turn O!

Turn, sin - ner, turn to - day, turn, sin - ner, turn O!
Turn, O sin - ner, de world da gwine, turn, sin - ner, turn O!

1st Variation

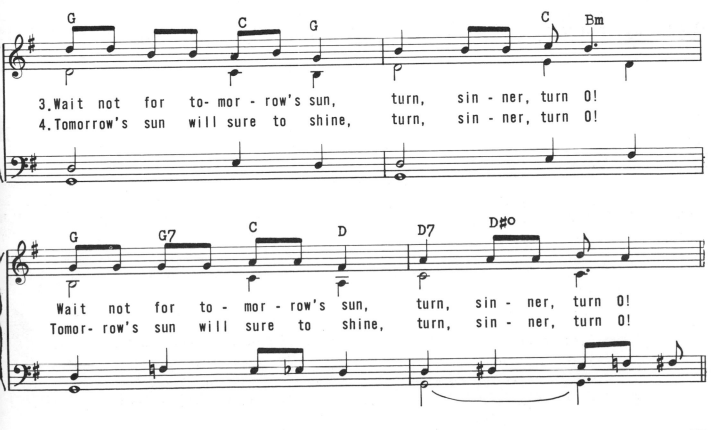

3. Wait not for to - mor - row's sun, turn, sin - ner, turn O!
4. Tomorrow's sun will sure to shine, turn, sin - ner, turn O!

Wait not for to - mor - row's sun, turn, sin - ner, turn O!
Tomor - row's sun will sure to shine, turn, sin - ner, turn O!

5. The sun may shine, but on your grave, turn, sin-ner, turn O! The

sun may shine, but on your grave, turn, sin-ner, turn O!

6. Hark! I hear dem sin-ner say, Turn, sin-ner, turn O!
7. If you get to heaven I'll get there too, Turn, sin-ner, turn O!

Hark! I hear dem sin-ner say, Turn, sin-ner, turn O!
If you get to heaven I'll get there too, Turn, sin-ner, turn O!

8. O   sin-ner, you   make mis - take,   Turn,   sin - ner, turn O!
9. While de lamp hold   out   to   burn,   Turn,   sin - ner, turn O!
10. De wile' sin- ner   may   re - turn,   Turn,   sin - ner, turn O!

O   sin-ner, you   make mis - take,   Turn,   sin - ner, turn O!
While de lamp hold   out   to   burn,   Turn,   sin - ner, turn O!
De wile' sin - ner   may   re - tuen,   Turn,   sin - ner, turn O!

11   Bro' Joe, you ought to know my name -
                                    Hallelujah.

12   My name is written in de book ob life.
13   If you look in de book you'll fin' 'em
                                    dar,

14   One mornin' I was a-walkin' down.
15   I saw de berry a-hinging down.
16   (Lord) I pick de berry , an' I suck
                                    de juice.

17   Jes' as sweet as de honey in de comb.
18   I wonder where Fader Jimmy gone.
19   My fader gone to de yonder worl'.
20   You dig de spring dat nebber dry.
21   De more I dig 'em, de water spring.
22   De water spring dat nebber dry.

My Army Cross Over

1. My brud-der, tik keer Sa- tan, My ar-my cross o - ber, My

brud-der, tik keer Sa - tan, My ar-my cross o - ber. My

ar - my cross o - ber, my ar-my cross o - ber, O

Pha-raoh's ar - my dround-ed, My ar-my cross o - ber, My

ar-my, my ar-my, my ar-my cross o - ber.

2 We'll cross de riber Jordan.
3 We'll cross de danger water.
4 We'll cross de mighty Myo.

Join The Angel Band

1. If you look up de road you see Fa- der Mo - sey

join de an - gel band, If you look up de road you

see Fa-der Mo - sey join de an - gel band.

2 Do, Fader Mosey, gader your army,
3 O do mo' soul gader togeder.
4 O do join 'em, join 'em for Jesus.
5 O do join 'em, join 'em archangel.

Cotton Wagon Train

I An' Satan Had A Race

1. I an' Sa - tan had a race, hal - le- lu, hal - le - lu,
I an' Sa - tan had a race, hal - le - lu, hal - le - lu.

2   Win de race agin de course.
3   Satan tell me to my face.
4   He will break my Kingdom down.
5   Jesus whisper in my heart.
6   He will build 'em up again.
7   Satan mount de iron grey.
8   Ride half way to Pilot-Bar.
9   Jesus mount de milk-white horse.
10   Say you cheat my Fader children,
11   Say you cheat 'em out of glory.
12   Trouble like a gloomy cloud.
13   Gader dick an' tunder loud.

Shall I Die?

1. Be - liev - er, O shall I die? O my ar - my, shall I die?

2. Je - sus die, shall I die? Die on the cross, shall I die?

3 Die, die, die, shall I die?
   Jesus da coming, shall I die?

4 Run for to meet him, shall I die?
   Weep like a weeper, shall I die?

5 Mourn like a mourner, shall I die?
   Cry like a crier, shall I die?

When We Do Meet Again

When we do meet a-gain, when we do meet a-gain, when we

do meet a-gain, 'Twill be no more to part. Broth-er Bil - ly,

fare you well, broth-er Bil -ly, fare you well, we'll

sing hal - le - lu -jah when we do meet a - gain.

The White Marble Stone

1. Sis -ter Dol- ly light the lamp, And the lamp light the road, And I

wish I been there for to yed - de Jor - dan roll.

2 O the city light the lamp,
        The white man he will sold;
   And I wish I been there, *etc.*

3 O the white marble stone,
        And the white marble stone.

Minor Variation

O my sis-ter, light the lamp, And the lamp light the road; _____ I

wish I been there for to hear-de Jor - dan roll.

I Can't Stand The Fire

I can't stan' de fire (dear sis-ter) I can't stan' de

fire, (O Lord), I can't stan' de fire, while Jor-dan da roll so

swif'.(Tid-dy Ri-nah.) Can't stan' de fire, can't stan' de fire,

can't stan' de fire, (O Lord)__ can't stan' de fire.

Meet, O Lord

1. Meet, O Lord, on de milk - white horse, an' de nine-teen wile* in his han'; Drop on, drop on de crown on my head, an' roll-y in my Je-sus arm. In dat morn-in' all day, in dat morn-in' all day, in dat morn-in' all

day   When   Je - sus de Chris' been   born.

2   Moon went into de poplar tree,
     An' star went into blood;
     In dat mornin', *etc.*

* *i.e. the anointing vial.*

Wait, Mr. Mackright

Wai',   Mis-ter Mack - right,   An' 'e yed-de what Sa - tan

say: Sa-tan, full me full of Mus- ic, An' tell me not to pray.

Mis-ter Mack-right, cry ho - ly!   O Lord,   cry ho - ly!

Early In The Morning

2   I meet my mudder early in de mornin';
      An' I ax her, how you do, my mudder?
        Walk 'em easy, *etc.*

3   I meet brudder Robert early in de
                       mornin',
      I ax brudder Robert, how you do,
                      my sonny?

4   I meet titta-Wisa early in de
                       mornin',
      I ax titta-Wisa, how you do, my darter?

Hail, Mary

I want some val-iant sol-dier here, I want some val-iant sol-dier here, I want some val-iant sol-dier here, To help me bear de cross. O hail, Ma-ry, hail! O hail, Ma-ry, hail! O hail, Ma-ry, hail! To help me bear de cross.

No More Rain Fall For Wet You

2   No more sun shine for burn you.
3   No more parting in de Kingdom.

4   No more backbiting in de Kingdom.
5   Every day shall be Sunday.

I Want To Go Home

In chanting style

2   Dere's no sun to burn you, - O yes, *etc.*
3   Dere's no hard trials,
4   Dere's no whips a-crackin',
5   Dere's no stormy weather.

6   Dere's no tribulation.
7   No more slavery in de Kingdom.
8   No evil-doers in de Kingdom.
9   All is gladness in de Kingdom.

Good-Bye, Brother

1. Good-bye, broth-er, Good-bye, broth-er, if I don't see you more;

Now God bless you, Now God bless you, if I don't see you more.

2 We part in de body, but we meet in de
                                    spirit,
   We'll meet in de heaben in de blessed
                                    Kingdom.

3 So good-bye, brother, good-bye, sister;
   Now God bless you, now God bless you.

Fare Ye Well

O fare you well, my brud-der, ——— Fare you well by de grace of God, For I'se gwin-en home; I'se gwin-en home, my Lord, I'se gwin-en home. Mas-sa Je-sus gib me a lit-tle broom, for to sweep my heart clean; Sweep 'em clean by de grace of God, An' glo-ry in my soul.

Many Thousand Go

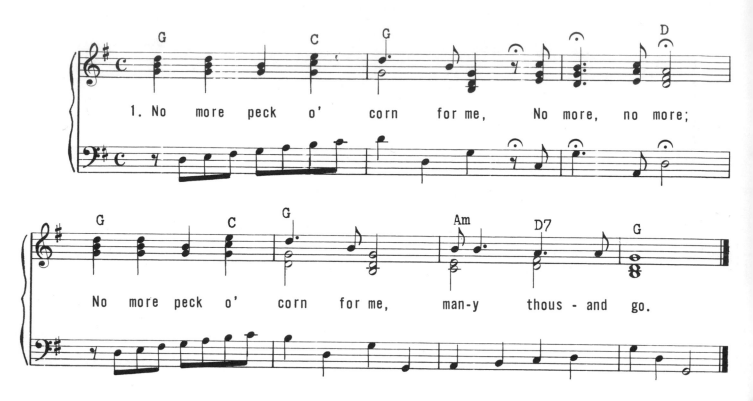

1. No more peck o' corn for me, No more, no more;

No more peck o' corn for me, man-y thous - and go.

2 No more driver's lash for me.
3 No more pint o' salt for me.

4 No more hundred lash for me.
5 No more mistress' call for me.

Brother Moses Gone

Brud-der Mo - ses came to de prom-ised land, Hal - le -

lu, hal - le - lu - - jah.

The Sin-Sick Soul

Brud-der George is a-gwine to glo-ry, Take car' de sin-sick soul, Brud-der George is a-gwine to glo-ry, Take car' de sin-sick soul, Brud-der Ste-phen's gwine to glo-ry, Take car' de sin-sick soul.

Some Valiant Soldier

Oh Lord, I want some val-i-ant sol-dier, I want some val-i-ant

sol-dier, I want some val-iant sol - dier, to help me bear de cross.

For I weep, I weep, I can't hold out; If

an - y mer - cy, Lord, O pit- y poor me.

Hallelu, Hallelu

1. Oh one day as an - od - er. Hal - le - lu, hal - le -

lu! 2.When de ship is out a - sail-in', Hal-le - lu - - jah!

3. Member walk and never tire.
4. Member walk Jordan long road.
5. Member walk tribulation.
6. You go home to Wappoo.

7. Member seek new repentance.
8. I go to seek my fortune.
9. I go to seek my dying Saviour.
10. You want to die like Jesus.

Children Do Linger

1.O mem-ber, will you lin-ger? See de chil-'en do

lin-ger here.2.I go to glo-ry wid you, ___ Mem-ber, join! ___

3   O Jesus is our captain.
4   He lead us on to glory.
5   We'll meet at Zion gateway.
6   We'll talk dis story over.
7   We'll enter into glory.
8   When we done wid dis world trials.
9   We done wid all our crosses.
10 O brudder, will you meet us?

11 When de ship is out a-sailin'.
12 O Jesus got de hellum.
13 Fader, gader in your chil'en.
14 O gader dem for Zion.
15 'Twas a beauteous Sunday mornin'.
16 When He rose from de dead.
17 He will bring you milk and honey.

Good-Bye

Good- bye, my brud-der, Good- bye, Hal - le - lu- jah! Good-

bye, sis-ter Sal - ly, Good - bye, Hal - le - lu- jah! Go - ing

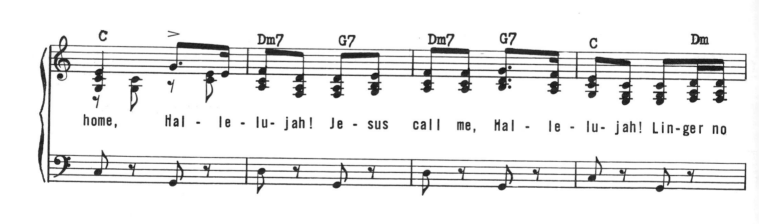

home, Hal - le - lu- jah! Je - sus call me, Hal - le - lu- jah! Lin-ger no

long-er, Hal - le - lu- jah! Tar- ry no long- er, Hal - le - lu- jah!

(This is generally sung at the end of a meeting.)

98

Lord, Make Me More Patient

Lord, make me more pa - tient,* Lord, make me more pa - - tient, Lord, make me more pa - tient, un - til we meet a - gain; ____ Pa - tient, pa - tient, pa - tient, un - til we meet ___ a - gain. ____

* Any adjective (like "holy", "loving", "peaceful", etc.,) may be used here.

Revolt on a Slave Ship

The Day Of Judgment

1. And de moon will turn to blood, And de moon will turn to

blood, And de moon will turn to blood in dat day. O

yoy, my soul! And de moon will turn to blood in dat day.

2   And you'll see de stars a-fallin'.
3   And de world will be on fire.
4   And you'll hear de saints a-singin'.
5   And de Lord will say to de sheep,
6   For to go to Him right hand;
7   But de goats must go to de left.

The Resurrection Morn

1. O run, Mary, run, Hal-le-lu,__ hal-le-lu! O run, Ma-ry, run, Hal-le-lu——jah! 2. It was ear-ly in de morn-in', Hal-le-lu,__ hal-le-lu! It was ear-ly in de morn-in', Hal-le-lu———jah!

3   That she went to the sepulchre,
4   And de Lord He wasn't da.
5   But she see a man a-comin',
6   And she thought it was de gardener.
7   But he say, "O touch me not,
8   "For I am not yet ascended.
9   "But tell to my disciples
10   "Dat de Lord He is arisen".
11   So run, Mary, run, *etc.*

Nobody Knows The Trouble I've Had

No-bo-dy knows de trou-ble I've had, No-bo-dy knows but

Je - sus; No-bo-dy knows de trou-ble I've had, (sing)

glo - ry hal - le - lu! 1. One morn-ing I was a-

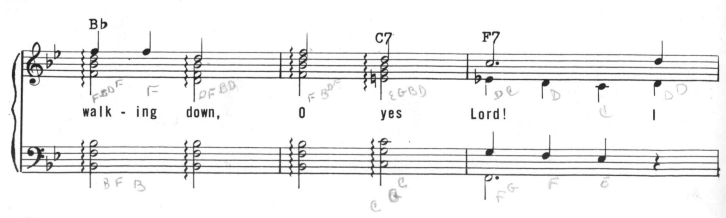

walk-ing down, O yes Lord! I

saw some ber - ries a - hang - ing down,　　O　yes　Lord!

2　I pick de berry and I suck de juice,
　　　O yes Lord!
　Just as sweet as de honey in de comb,
　　　O yes Lord!

3　Sometimes I'm up, sometimes I'm down,
　Sometimes I'm almost on de groun'.

4　What make de Satan hate me so?
　Because he got me once and he let me go.

The Discovery of Nat Turner

Who Is On The Lord's Side

2 Weepin' Mary.
3 Mournin' Marta.
4 Risen-Jesus.

Hold Out To The End

All dem Mount Zion mem- ber, day have man-y ups and downs; ___ But

cross come or no come, for to hold out to the end.

Hold out to the end, ___ hold out to the end, ___ It

is my 'ter- mi - na - tion for to hold out to the end.

Come Go With Me

1. Ole Sa-tan is a bus-y ole man, he roll stones in my way; Mass' Je-sus is my bos-om friend, He roll 'em out o' my way. O come-e go wid me, O come-e go wid me, O come-e go wid me, A-walk-in' in de heav-en I roam.

2. I did not come here myself, my Lord,
   It was my Lord who brought me here;
   And I really do believe I'm a child
   of God,
   A-walkin' in de heaven I roam.
   O come-e go wid me, (etc.)

One cold freez-ing morn - ing I lay dis bo - dy

down, I will pick up my cross an'__ fol-low my Lord all

roun' my fa- der's throne. 1. Ev-ery hour in de day cry

ho - ly, cry ho- ly, my Lord! Ev-ery hour in de day cry

2 Every hour in de night cry Jesus, *etc.*

In The Mansions Above

Good Lord, in de man - shans a - bove, Good Lord, in de man - shans a - bove, My Lord, I hope to meet my Je - sus in de man-shans a-bove. 1. If you get to heav- en be - fore I do, Lord, Tell my

Je- sus I'm a-com - in' too, To de man - shans a- bove.

2 My Lord, I've had many crosses an' trials
    here below;
  My Lord, I hope to meet you
    In de manshans above.

3 Fight on, my brudder, for de manshans
    above,
  For I hope to meet my Jesus dere
    In de manshans above.

Shout On, Children

1. Shout on, chil-'en, you nev- er die; Glo - ry hal- le - lu!

You in de Lord, an' de Lord in you; Glo - ry hal- le - lu!

2 Shout an' pray both night an' day;
  How can you die, you in de Lord?

3 Come on chil'en, let's go home;
  O I'm so glad you're in de Lord.

Jesus, Won't You Come By-And-Bye!

You ride dad horse, you call him Mac - a - do - ni,

Je - sus, won't you come bum - by? You ride him in de

morn - in' and you ride him in de eve - nin', Je - sus, won't you come bum -

by? De Lord knows de world's gwine to end up,

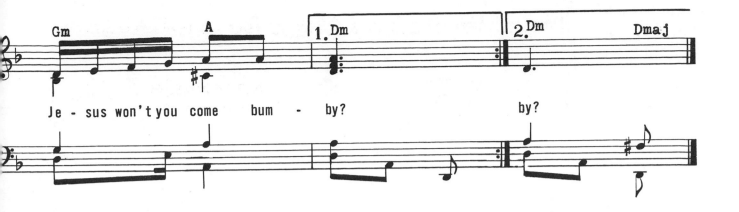

Je - sus won't you come bum - by? by?

Heave Away

Heave a - way, _____ heave a - way! _____ I'd

rath- er court a yel-low gal than work for Hen- ry Clay, Heave a - way, _____

heave a - way! _____ Yel- low gal, I want to go, I'd

rath-er court a yel-low gal than work for Hen - ry Clay.

Heave a - way! _____ Yel - low gal, I want to go!

Wake Up, Jacob

1.Wake up, Ja - cob, day is a-break - ing, I'm on my

way; _____ O, wake up, Ja - cob, day is a-break - ing, I'm

on my way. O! way. I want to go to heav - en when I die,— do love de Lord! I want to go to heav - en when I die,— do love de Lord! I Lord!

2. Got some friends on de oder shore,
Do love de Lord!
I want to see 'em more an' more,
Do love de Lord!
Wake up, Jacob, *(etc.)*

Pressing Cotton for Bales

On To Glory

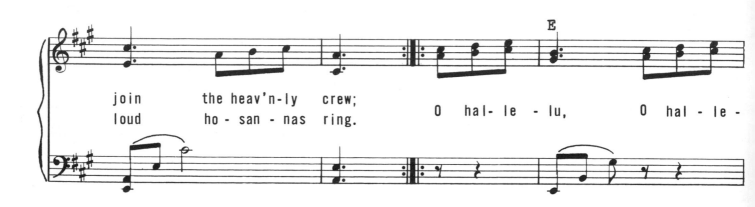

1. {
O come my breth-ren and sis-ters, too, we're gwine to
To Christ our Sav - - iour let us sing, and make our

join the heav'n-ly crew;
loud ho-san-nas ring.

O hal-le-lu, O hal-le-

lu, O hal-le-lu - jah to the world. *(repeat)*

2. Oh, there's Bill Thomas, I know him well,
   He's got to work to keep from hell;
   He's got to pray by night and day,
   If he wants to go by the narrow way.

3. There's Chloe Williams, she makes me mad,
   For you see, I know she's going on bad;
   She told me a lie this arternoon,
   And the devil will get her very soon.

Just Now

1. Sanc-ti-fy me, sanc-ti-fy me, sanc-ti-fy me, sanc-ti-fy me, sanc-ti-fy me just now, just now, just now; Sanc-ti-fy me just now.

2. Good religion, good religion, *(etc.)*
3. Come to Jesus, come to Jesus, *(etc.)*

Shock Along, John

Loo, loo, loo, loo, loo, loo, loo, shock a-long, John, shock a-long;

Loo, loo, loo, loo, loo, loo, loo, shock a-long, John, shock a-long.

Round The Corn, Sally

1. Five can't ketch me and ten can't hold me, ho _____

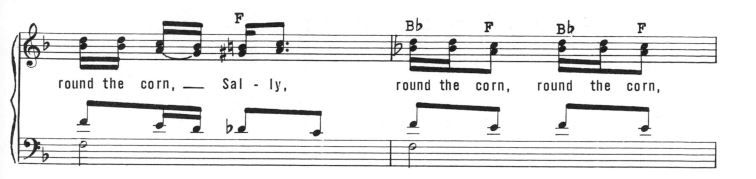

round the corn, __ Sal - ly, round the corn, round the corn,

round the corn, Sal-ly! Ho, ho, ho, round the corn, Sal-ly!

2. Here's your iggle-quarter and here's
   your count-aquils

3. I can bank, 'ginny bank, 'ginny bank
   the weaver.

Jordan's Mills

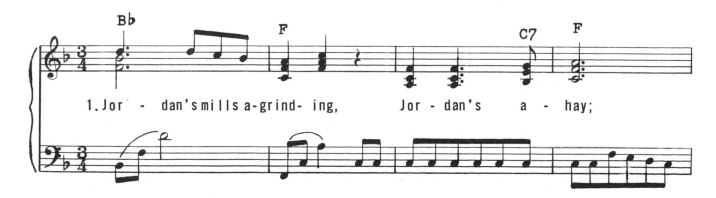

1. Jor - dan's mills a-grind- ing, Jor - dan's a - hay;

2. Built without nail or hammer.
3. Runs without wind or water.

Sabbath Has No End

1. Gwine to walk a-bout Zi - on, I real-ly do be-lieve; walk a-bout Zi - on, I real-ly do be-lieve; walk a-bout Zi - on, I real-ly do be-lieve; Sab - bath has no end.

I do view one an-gel in one an-gel stand;__ Let's

mark him right down with the fore - half, with the harp-ess in his hand.

2. Gwine to follow King Jesus, I really
   do believe.
3. I love God certain.
4. My sister's got religion.
5. Set down in the Kingdom.
6. Religion is a fortune.

I Don't Feel Weary

I don't feel__ wea-ry and__ no-ways tired,__

O ___ glo-ry hal-le - lu - jah. 1.Jest let me in the King-dom while the

world is all on fire. ___ O glo-ry hal-le - lu - - jah.

2. Gwine to live with God forever, while *(etc.)*
3. And keep the ark a-moving, while *(etc.)*

Slave Cabin

The Hypocrite And The Concubine

1.Hyp - o - crite and the con - cu - bine __ liv - in' a - mong the

swine, __ They run to God with the lips and tongue, __ And

leave all the heart be - hind. Aunt-ie did you hear when

Je - sus rose? _____ Did you hear when Je - sus rose?

Aunt-ie did you hear when Je - sus rose? __ He rose and He 'scend on high.

O Shout Away

O shout, O shout, O shout a-way, and don't you mind, And

glo - ry, glo - ry, glo-ry in my soul! 1. And when 'twas night, I thought 'twas day, I

thought I'd pray my soul a-way, And glo - ry, glo - ry, glo-ry in my soul.

2. O Satan told me not to pray,
   He want my soul at Judgment Day.

3. And everywhere I want to pray,
   There something was in my way.

O'er The Crossing

1. Bend-in' knees a-ach-in', Bo-dy racked wid pain, I wish I was a child of God, I'd git home bime - - bye. Keep pray-in' I do be-lieve we're a long time wag-gin' o' de cross-in'; Keep pray-in' I do be-lieve we'll git home to heav-en bime - bye.

2. O yonder's my ole mudder. Been a-waggin'
   at de hill so long;
   It's about time she cross over. Git home
   bime bye.
   Keep prayin', I do believe, (etc.)

3. O hear dat lumberin' thunder A-roll from
   do' to do',
   A-callin' de people home to God; Dey'll
   git home bime-bye.
   Little chil'n, I do believe, (etc.)

4. O see dat forked lightnin' A-jump from
   cloud to cloud,
   A-pickin' up God's chil'n; Dey'll
   git home bime-bye.
   Pray, mourner, I do believe, (etc.)

Rock O' My Soul

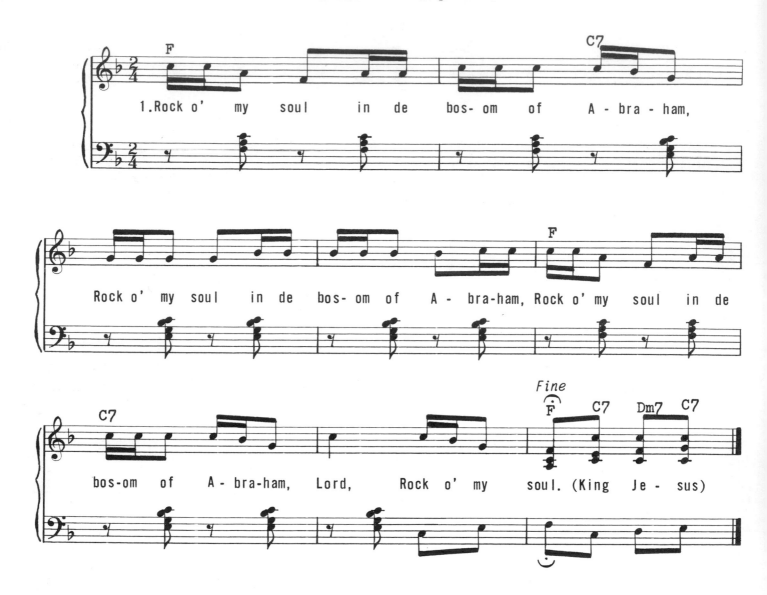

1. Rock o' my soul in de bos-om of A-bra-ham, Rock o' my soul in de bos-om of A-bra-ham, Rock o' my soul in de bos-om of A-bra-ham, Lord, Rock o' my soul. (King Je-sus)

Fine

2. He toted the young lambs in his bosom
   (3 times)
   And leave the old sheep alone.

We Will March Through The Valley

1. We will march through the val - ley in peace, _____ We will march thru the val - ley in peace; _____ If Je - sus Him-self be our lead - er, We will march thru the val - ley in peace.

2. We will march, *(etc.)*
   Behold, I give myself away, and
   We will march, *(etc.)*

3. We will march, *(etc.)*
   This track I'll see and I'll pursue;
   We will march, *(etc.)*

4. We will march, *(etc.)*
   When I'm dead and buried in the
          cold, silent tomb,
   I don't want you to grieve for me.

What A Trying Time

1. O A-dam, where — are you? A - dam, where are you? A -
dam, where are you? O what a try - ing time!

2. Lord, I am in the garden.
3. Adam, you ate that apple
4. Lord, Eve gave it to me.
5. Adam, it was forbidden.
6. Lord said, walk out de garden.

Almost Over

1. Some seek de Lord and they don't seek Him right,

2. Sister, if your heart is warm,
Snow and ice will do you no harm.

3. I done been down, and I done been tried,
I been through the water, and I been
baptized.

4. O sister, you must mind how you step on
the cross,
Your feet might slip, and your soul get
lost.

5. And when you get to heaven, you'll be able
for to tell
How you shunned the gates of hell.

6. Wrestle with Satan and wrestle with sin,
Stepped over hell and come back agin.

Don't Be Weary, Traveller

Don't be wea - ry, trav - el-ler, Come a-long home to

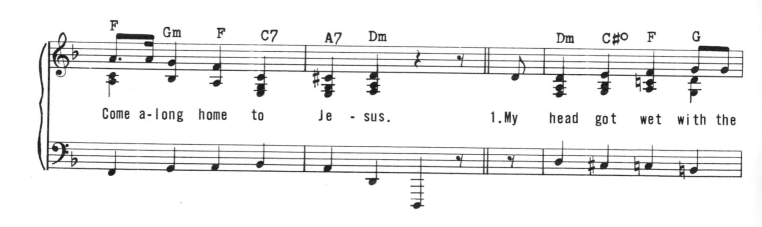

Je - sus. Don't be wea - ry, trav - el-ler,

Come a-long home to Je - sus. 1.My head got wet with the

mid- night dew, Come a-long home to Je - sus;

128

An -gels bear me wit-ness, too, Come a-long home to Je - sus.

2. Where to go I did not know,
   Ever since He freed my soul.

3. I look at de worl' and de worl' look new,
   I look at de worl' and de worl' look new.

Let God's Saints Come In

Come down, An-gel, and trou-ble the wa-ter, Come down, an-gel, and

trou-ble the wa-ter, Come down, an-gel, and trou-ble the wa-ter, And

let God's saints come in.   (God say you must)   1. Ca-naan land is the

land for me,   And let God's saints come   in.   Ca-naan land is the

land for   me,   And   let God's saints   come   in.

2. There was a wicked man,
   He kept them children in Egypt Land.

3. God did say to Moses one day,
   Say, Moses, go to Egypt Land,

4. And tell him to let my people go.
   And Pharaoh would not let 'em go.

5. God did go to Moses' house,
   And God did tell him who He was,

6. God and Moses walked and talked,
   And God did show him who He was.

The Golden Altar

John saw-r, _____ John _____ saw-r, O _____ John saw de

ho - ly num - ber set - tin' on de gold - en al - tar!

1. It's a lit-tle while long- er yere be - low, yere be-low, yere be-low, It's a

lit-tle while long - er yere be- low, be - fore de lamb of God!

2. And home to Jesus we will go,
      we will go, *(etc.)*
   We are de people of de Lord.
      John saw-r, *(etc.)*

3. Dere's a golden slipper in de heavens
      for you, *(etc.)*
   Before de Lamb of God.

4. I wish I'd been dere when prayer begun,
      (etc.)

5. To see my Jesus about my sins, *(etc.)*

6. Then home to glory we will go, *(etc.)*

The Winter

O de vin-ter,   O de vin-ter,   O de vin-ter'll soon be

o - ber, chil-len, De vin-ter,   O de vin-ter,   O de vin-ter'll soon be

o - ber, chil-len, De vin-ter,   O de vin-ter,   O de vin-ter'll soon be

o-ber, chil-len, yes, my Lord! 'Tis Paul and Si - las bound in chains, chains, and

one did weep, and de od-er one did pray, od-er one did pray.

2. You bend your knees on holy ground, ground,
   And ask de Lord, Lord for to turn
                    you around.
         For de vinter, (etc.)

3. I turn my eyes towards the sky, sky,
   And ask de Lord, Lord for wings to fly.

4. For you see me gwine 'long so, so,
   I has my tri-trials yer below.

The Heaven Bells

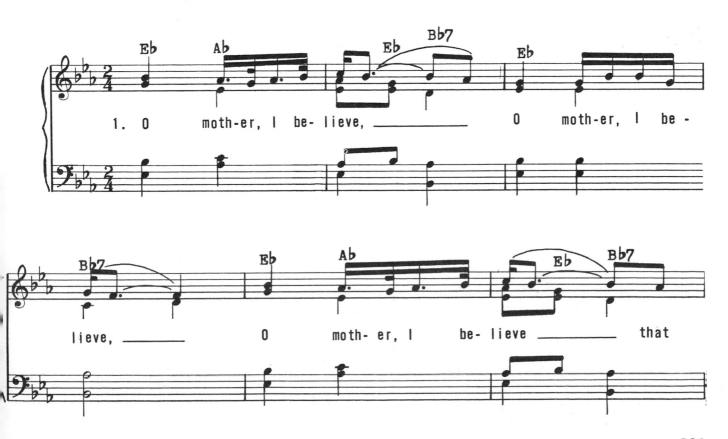

1. O moth-er, I be- lieve, _____ O moth-er, I be-

lieve, _____ O moth-er, I be- lieve _____ that

Christ was_ cru - ci - fied! O don't you hear the heav-en bells a -

ring - ing o - ver me, a - ring - ing o - ver me, a -

ring - ing o - ver me? O don't you hear the heav- en bells a -

ring-ing o - ver me? It sounds like the Judg-ment Day!

The Gold Band

1. Gwine to march a - way in de gold band, in de ar - my, bye and bye; Gwine to march a - way in de gold band, in de ar - my, bye and bye. Sin - ner, what you gwine to do dat day? Sin-ner, what you gwine to do dat day? When de fire's a -

roll - ing be-hind you, in de ar - my bye and bye.

2. Sister Mary gwine to hand down the robe,
   In the army, bye-and-bye;
   Gwine to hand down the robe and the
   gold band,
   In the army, bye-and-bye.

The Good Old Way

As I went down in de val-ley to pray, ___ stud-y-ing a-bout dat

good old way, When you shall wear de star - ry crown, ___

Good Lord, show me de way. O mourn-er, let's go down,

let's go down, let's go down, O mourn - er,

let's go down, down in de val-ley to pray.

I'm Going Home

1. I sought my Lord in de wil-der-ness, in de wil-der-ness, in de

2. I found free grace in de wilderness.
3. My Father preaches in de wilderness.

Sinner Won't Die No More

O de lamb done been down here an' died, De lamb done been down here an' died, O de lamb done been down here an' died, Sin-ner won't die no mo'.

1. I won- der what bright an - gels, an - gels, an - gels, I won- der what bright an - gels, de robes all read-y now.

2. O see dem ships come a-sailing,
   sailing, sailing,
O see dem ships come a-sailing,
De robes all ready now.

Brother, Guide Me Home

Brud-der, guide me home an' I am glad, Bright an-gels bid-dy me to

come;   Brud-der, guide me home an' I am glad, Bright

an-gels bid-dy me to come.   1.What a hap-py time,

chil-'n, What a hap-py time, chil-'n, What a

hap - py time, chil - 'n, Bright an - gels bid-dy me to come.

2. Let's go to God, chil'n, *(3 times)*
Bright angels biddy me to come.

Little Children, Then Won't You Be Glad?

1. Lit-tle chil-dren, then won't you be glad, Lit-tle chil-dren, then won't you be

glad, That you have been to Heav'n, An' you're gwine to go a- gain, For to

try _ on the long white robe, _ chil-dren, for to try _ on the long white robe.

2. King Jesus, he was so strong, *(3 times)*
   my Lord,
   That He jarred down the walls of hell.

3. Don't you hear what the chariot say?
   (twice)
   De fore wheels run by de grace ob God,
   An' de hind wheels dey run by faith.

4. Don't you 'member what you promise
   de Lord? *(twice)*
   You promise de Lord that you would feed
   His sheep,
   An' gather His lambs so well.

Charleston Gals

1. As I walked down the new-cut road, I met the tap and then the toad; The toad com-menced to whis-tle and sing, And the pos-sum cut the pig-eon wing. A-long came an old man

rid-ing by: Old man, if you don't mind, your horse will die;

If he dies, we'll tan his skin, And if he lives, we'll ride him a-gin.

Hi, ho, for Charles-ton gals! Charles-ton gals are the gals for me.

2. As I went a-walking down the street,
Up steps Charleston gals to take a walk with me.
I kep' a-walking and they kep' a-talking,
I danced with a gal with a hole in her stocking.

Slaves on Edisto Island, South Carolina (1862).

Run, Nigger, Run

O some tell me that a nig- ger won't steal, But I've seen a nig-ger in my corn-field; O run, nig-ger, run, for the pat- rol will catch you, O run, nig-ger, run, for 'tis al - most day.

Former slaves, after Emancipation Proclamation, approaching Union Territory. Sketch by Edwin Forbes.

I'm Gwine To Alabamy

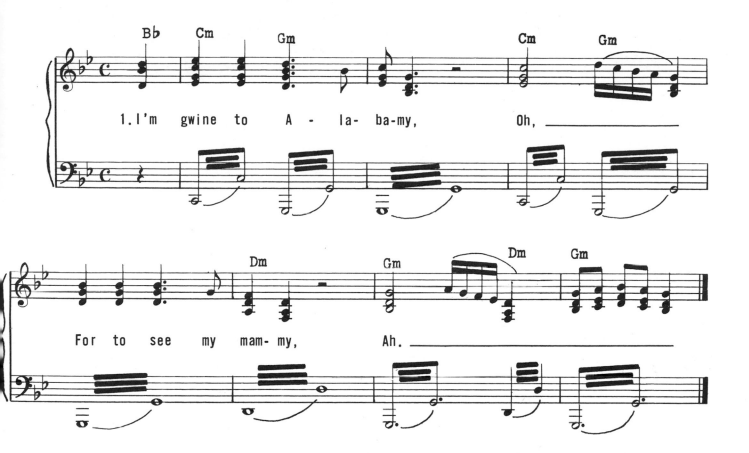

1. I'm gwine to A - la - ba-my, Oh, _____
For to see my mam-my, Ah. _____

2. She went from ole Virginny, - Oh,
   And I'm her pickaninny, - Ah.

3. She lives on the Tombigbee, - Oh,
   I wish I had her wid me, - Ah.

4. Now I'm a good big nigger, - Oh,
   I reckon I won't git bigger, - Ah.

5. But I'd like to see my mammy, - Oh,
   Who lives in Alabamy, - Ah.

On the Deck of a Slave Ship

My Father, How Long?

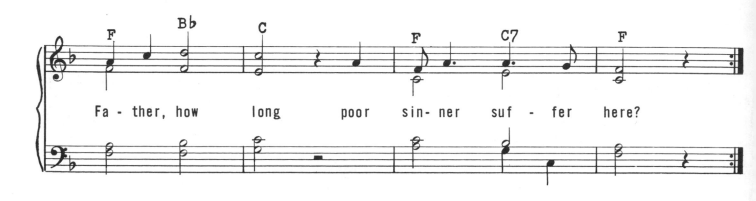

2. We'll soon be free, *(3 times)*
   De Lord will call us home.

3. We'll walk de miry road,
   When pleasure never dies.

4. We'll walk de golden streets
   Of de New Jerusalem.

5. My brudders do sing
   De praises of de Lord.

6. We'll fight for liberty
   When de Lord will call us home.

I'm In Trouble

O Daniel

O Brothers, Don't Get Weary

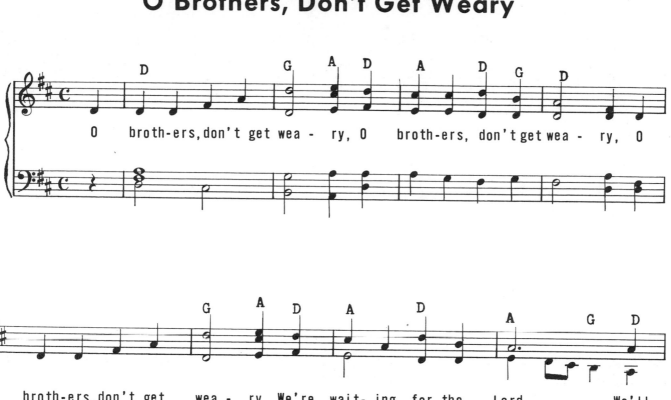

O broth-ers, don't get wea - ry, O broth-ers, don't get wea - ry, O

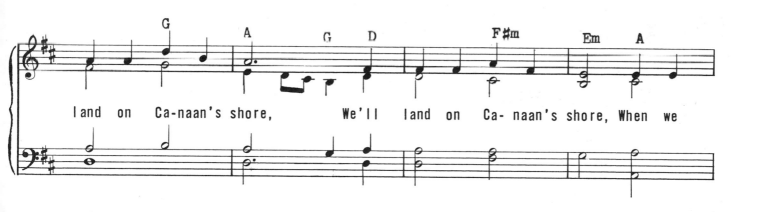

broth-ers, don't get wea - ry, We're wait-ing for the Lord. We'll

land on Ca-naan's shore, We'll land on Ca-naan's shore, When we

land on Ca-naan's shore, we'll meet for-ev-er more.

I Want To Join The Band

What is that up yon-der I see? Two lit-tle an-gels com-in' a'-ter me; I want to join the band, I want to join the band (sing togeth-er,) I want to join the band.

"Come and Join Us Brothers." Negro Regiment from the Civil War.

Jacob's Ladder

I want to climb up Ja-cob's lad - - der, Ja-cob's lad - - der, O Ja-cob's lad - - der, I want to climb up Ja-cob's lad - - der, But I can't climb it till I make my peace with the Lord. O — praise ___ ye the Lord, I'll praise Him till I die, I'll praise Him till I die, and sing Je - ru - sa - lem.

Pray On

Pray on, pray on, pray on dem light us

o - ver; Pray on, pray on, de u - nion break of day.

My ___ sis-ter, you come to see bap-tize, in de u - nion break of day;

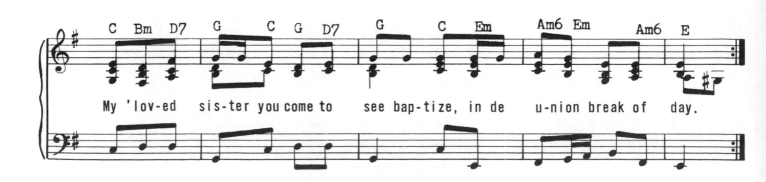

My 'lov-ed sis-ter you come to see bap-tize, in de u-nion break of day.

Good News, Member

Good news, mem- ber, good news mem-ber, Don't you mind what Sa - tan say;

Good news, mem- ber, good news, And I heard- e from Heav'n to - day.

1. My brud-der have a seat and I so glad, Good news, mem- ber, good news; My

brud-der have a seat and I so glad, And I heard-e from Heav'n to - day.

2. Mr. Hawley have a home in Paradise.
3. Archangel bring baptizing down.

I Want To Die Like-A Lazarus Die

Tit- ty 'rit - ta
I want to die like-a Laz - 'rus die,

die like-a Laz - 'rus die; I want to die like-a Laz - 'rus

die, like-a Laz - 'rus die, like-a Laz - 'rus die.

Away Down In Sunbury

O mas-sa take dat new bran coat and hang it on de wall.
Dat dark-ee take dat same ole coat and wear 'em to de ball.

O don't you hear my true lub sing? O don't you hear 'em sigh? A-
way ___ down in Sun - bu-ry I'm bound to live and die.

This Is The Trouble Of The World

I ax Fa-der Geor-gy for re - li - gion, Fa - der
Geor-gy would - n't give me re - li - gion. You ___

give me re-li-gion for to run to my el-der; O dis is de trou-ble of de world. *Fine* Dis is de trou-ble of de world, O, Dis is de trou-ble of de world.

What you doubt for?
shame

Take it ea-sy.
Tit-ty 'Me-lia.

D.C.

Lean On The Lord's Side

1. Wai', poor Dan-iel, he lean on de Lord's side;(say)

Dan - iel rock de Li - on jaw, lean on de Lord's side.

Ab7 Eb   Gm   Cm

2. (Say)De gold- en chain to ease him down.

3. De silver spade to dig his grave;
   He lean, *etc.*

These Are All My Father's Children

Dese all my Fa - der's chil- dren, Dese all my Fa- der's chil-dren,Dese all my Fa-der's chil-dren,out-shine de sun.

My Fa-der's done wid de trou-ble o' de world, wid de trou-ble o' de world, wid de trou-ble o' de world, My Fa-der's done wid de trou-ble o' de world, out-shine de sun.

The Old Ship Of Zion

Maryland Version

1. What ship is that you're en - list - ed up -on?

1. Don't you see that ship a - sail - in', a - sail - in', a - sail - in', Don't you see that ship a - sail - in', Gwine o - ver to the prom - ised land? I asked my Lord, shall I ev - er be the one, shall I ev - er be the one, shall I ev - er be the one to go sail - in', sail - in', sail - in', sail - in', Gwine o - ver to the prom - ised land?

2. She sails like she is heavy loaded.
3. King Jesus is the Captain.
4. The Holy Ghost is the Pilot.

O glo-ry hal-le-lu - jah! 'Tis the old ship of Zi - on, hal-le-

lu - jah! 'Tis the old ship of Zi- on, hal-le - lu - jah!

2. And who is the Captain of the ship
that you're on?
O glory, *etc.*
My Saviour is the Captain, hallelujah!

Come Along, Moses

Come a-long, Mo - ses, don't get lost, don't get lost, don't get lost, —

don't get lost, Come a-long, Mo - ses, don't get lost, We

are   the peo-ple of   God.   1. We   have a just   God   to

plead- a our cause,   to plead-a our cause,   to plead- a our cause,   We

have   a   just God   to plead-a our   cause, We   are   the   peo-ple of   God.

2. He sits in the Heaven and He answers
                                    prayer.
3. Stretch out your rod and come across.

Branding of Slaves

The Social Band

Bright an-gels on the wa - ter, Hover-ing by the light; Poor sin-ner stand in the dark - ness, And can-not see the light. I want Aunt-ie Ma-ry for to go with me, I want Aunt-ie Ma-ry for to go with me, I want Aunt-ie Ma-ry for to go with me, to join the so-cial band.

God Got Plenty O' Room

God got plen-ty o' room, got plen-ty o' room, 'Way in de King-dom, God got plen-ty o' room, My Je-sus say, 'Way in de King-dom. 1. Breth-ren I have come a-gain, 'Way in de King-dom, To help you all to pray and sing, 'Way in de King-dom.

2. So many a week and days have passed
Since we met together last.

3. Old Satan tremble when he sees
The weakest saints upon their knees.

4. Prayer makes the darkest cloud withdraw,
Prayer climbed the ladder Jacob saw.

5. Daniel's wisdom may I know,
Stephen's faith and spirit sure.

6. John's divine communion feel,
Joseph's meek and Joshua's zeal.

7. There is a school on earth begun,
Supported by the Holy one.

8. We soon shall lay our school-books by,
And shout salvation as I fly.

You Must Be Pure And Holy

You must be pure and ho-ly, You must be pure an'-a - ho - ly, You must be pure and ho-ly to see God feed his lambs.

rit.

3. The Devil am a liar and conjurer, too,
   My Lord *etc.*
   If you don't look out, he'll conjure you
   My Lord, *etc.*   through,

4. O run up, sonny, and get your crown
   And by your Father sit you down.

5. I was pretty young when I began,
   But now my work is almost done.

6. The Devil's mad and I am glad,
   He lost his soul he thought he had.

7. Go 'way, Satan, I don't mind you,
   You wonder, too, that you can't go through.

8. A lily- white stone came rolling down,
   It rolled like thunder through the town.

Belle Layotte

Mo dé- jà rou- lé tout la côte, Pan-cor ouar par - eil

belle La - yotte. *Fine* 1. Mo rou-lé tout la côte,

Mo rou- lé tout la col - o - nie, Mo pan- cor ouar

grif- fonne la qua mo gout comme la belle La - yotte.

2. Jean Babet, mon ami,
   Si vous couri par en haut
   Vous mandé belle Layotte
   Cadeau la li té promi mouin.

3. Domestique la maison
   Ye tout faché avec mouin
   Paraporte chanson la
   Mo composé pou la belle Layotte.

Remon

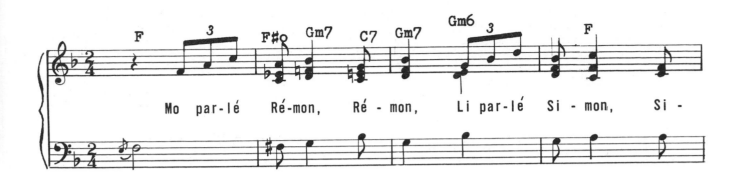

Mo par-lé Ré-mon, Ré - mon, Li par-lé Si - mon, Si -

mon li par-lé Ti - tine, Ti - tine, li tom- bé dans cha-grin.

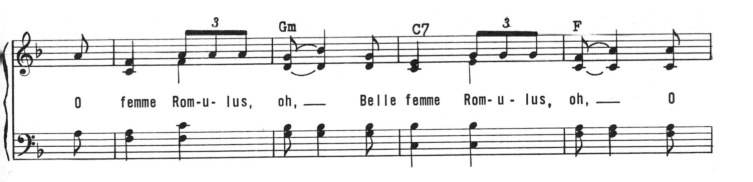

O femme Rom-u- lus, oh, — Belle femme Rom-u- lus, oh, — O

femme Rom- u- lus, oh, — Belle femme qui ça vou- lé mo fai.

Li pas man-dé robe mous-se-line, li pas man-dé dé - ba bro-dé, Li

Aurore Bradaire

Au - rore Bra - daire

belle ti fille, Au - rore Bra-daire, belle ti fille, Au - rore Bra-daire,

belle ti fille, C'est li ma ou-lé, c'est li ma pren.

Fine

Am F Em7 Dm G7 1. C 2.C *D.C.*

pas man-dé sou- lier prin-elle, C'est li mo ou- lé, c'est li ma pren. li ma pren.

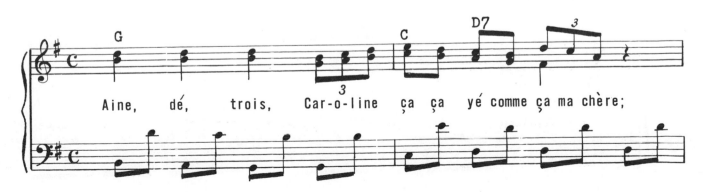

Caroline

G C D7

Aine, dé, trois, Car-o-line ça ça yé comme ça ma chère;

Aine, dé, trois, Car- o - line ça ça yè comme ça ma chère.

Pa - pa di-non, Man-mandi non, C'est li mo oulé, c'est li ma pren; ya

pas l'ar-zan pou ach-té ca-banne, C'est li mo ou - le, c'est li ma pren.

Calinda

1. Mi - chié pré - val li don - nin gran bal, Li fait

naig pa - yé pou sau - té in-pé Dan - sé Ca-lin-da, bou -

doum, bou - doum, Dan - sé Ca-lin-da, bou - doum, bou - doum.

2. Michié Préval li té capitaine bal,
   So cocher Louis té maite cérémonie.

3. Dans léquirie la yavé gran gala,
   Mo cré choual layé té bien étonné.

4 Yavé des négresse belle passé maitresse,
   Yé volé bébelle dans l'ormoire mamzelle.

Lolotte

Pauve pi-ti Lo-lotte a mouin, Pauve pi-ti Lo-lotte a mouin,

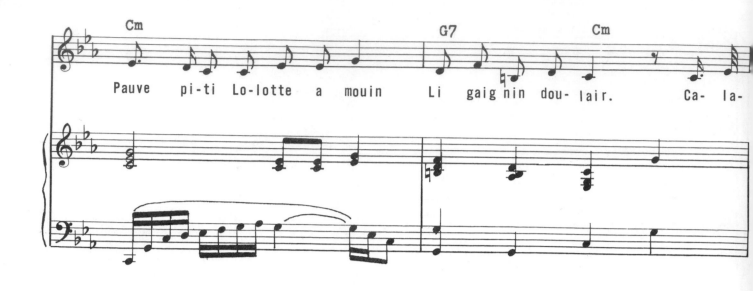

Pauve pi-ti Lo-lotte a mouin Li gaig nin dou-lair. Ca-la-

lou por-té ma-drasse, li por-té ji-pon gar-ni, Ca-la-

lou por-té ma-drasse li por-té ji-pon gar-ni.

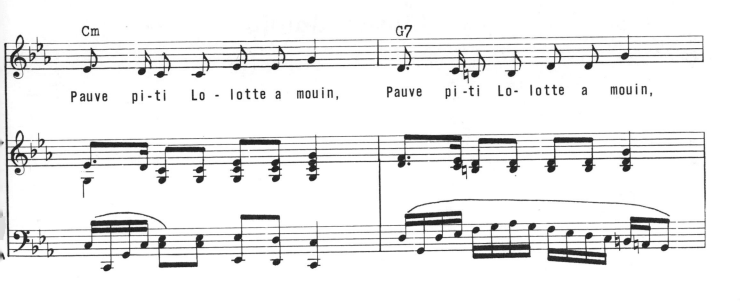

Pauve pi-ti Lo- lotte a mouin, Pauve pi-ti Lo- lotte a mouin,

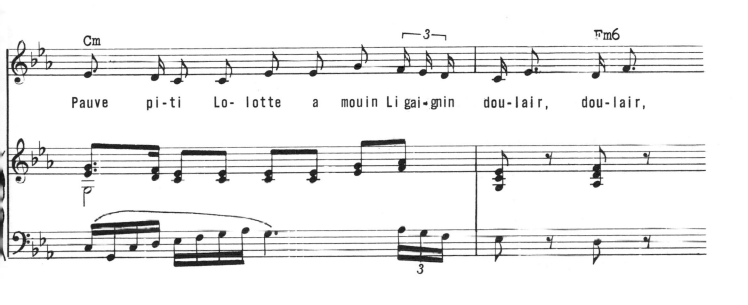

Pauve pi-ti Lo- lotte a mouin Li gai-gnin dou-lair, dou-lair,

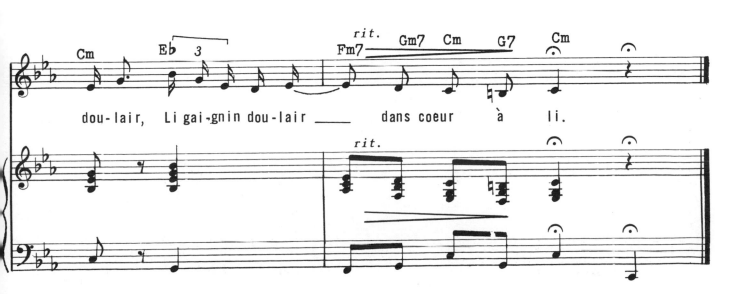

dou-lair, Li gai-gnin dou-lair ____ dans coeur à li.

Musieu Bainjo

Vo-yez   ce mu- let,   là mu - sieu Bain-jo,

comme il est in -so - lent.   Cha-peau sur cô - té,   mu-sieu Bain-jo,

La canne à la main,
Botte qui fait crin, crin,

INDEX TO SONGS